# Bound Water
## in
# Biological Integrity

# Bound Water
# in
# Biological Integrity

*By*

**S. J. WEBB, D.I.C., Ph.D. (Lond.)**

*Associate Professor of Microbiology*
*Department of Bacteriology*
*University of Saskatchewan*
*Saskatoon, Saskatchewan, Canada*

CHARLES C THOMAS · PUBLISHER
*Springfield · Illinois · U.S.A.*

*Published and Distributed Throughout the World by*
CHARLES C THOMAS • PUBLISHER
Bannerstone House
301-327 East Lawrence Avenue, Springfield, Illinois, U.S.A.
Natchez Plantation House
735 North Atlantic Boulevard, Fort Lauderdale, Florida, U.S.A.

© *1965, by* CHARLES C THOMAS • PUBLISHER
Library of Congress Catalog Card Number: 65-18067

*With THOMAS BOOKS careful attention is given to all details of manufacturing and design. It is the Publisher's desire to present books that are satisfactory as to their physical qualities and artistic possibilities and appropriate for their particular use. THOMAS BOOKS will be true to those laws of quality that assure a good name and good will.*

*Printed in the United States of America*
*N-1*

*To the late Dr. S. E. Jacobs of Imperial College*
*a wonderful man to whom I owe so much*

# PREFACE

I N THE LAST SEVENTY YEARS, our knowledge of the metabolic cycles by which a cell lives has increased enormously. Almost daily, it becomes necessary to modify metabolic charts or add a new enzyme to lecture notes. As the number of enzymes mount and the complexities of synthesis and genetic continuity become better understood so the distance between the test tube and the living cell should shorten. Today we are accustomed to explanations of biological processes in terms of atoms and molecules; to the vast number of skillful investigators who continually prod and poke, ever seeking that little extra piece of knowledge, and to the explosion of biology into many small fragments. No one can doubt the enthusiasm with which most of these researchers tackle their problems, or the value of their work, but there is the ever present danger of "too many cooks. . . ." It is from the fragmentation of biology that the danger springs. The divisions are now so numerous that they are rapidly approaching the ridiculous, yet the necessity of bringing them together is obvious to all. The job of applying the brakes, or keeping things in reasonable perspective, must inevitably fall on the biologist. Today he should be trained,

or train himself, in such things as quantum mechanics, thermodynamics and molecular structure, but he must still think as a
biologist. He should collect the information fed to him and view
it in terms of his own knowledge as to the types of cells, and the
factors which affect their life and death.

Biochemical discoveries have revealed many similarities in the
metabolism of different microbial, plant and animal cells, and
studies of genetics have done likewise. The molecular structure
of some large and complex molecules are now known but because
of their intricate designs the suggested mechanism by which they
are said to function are becoming equally complicated. Every well
trained biologist believes the unity of the living processes to be
simple and although through the process of organic evolution
these large and wonderful molecules have evolved, their role must
be to simplify and stabilize the processes that constitute life. Today, we are able to break open a cell by very gentle treatment and
study this or that molecule, but the solution we obtain will not
reform into a cell or make a new one. Also, when we study
enzymes isolated from cells able to grow at temperatures above
70 degrees C., their characteristics are no different from those obtained from a cell killed by such temperatures, and we must ask
ourselves why. There is also the very topical DNA. If, as proposed,
its structure is common to all cells, so must its mode of action.
Why then are there differences in the mutation rate of a given
character in different cells and the ease with which these cells are
damaged by ultraviolet or ionizing radiation? From such questions, it would seem that the biological integrity of these macromolecules relies not only on their structure but also on that of
other molecules with which they are associated in the living cell.

These questions, and the knowledge that the vast majority of
metabolic processes rely on nothing more than the addition or
subtraction of water molecules, prompted the work in our laboratories. To us, it seemed illogical to think that the major role of
water was to carry metabolites into and out of cells and that the
hydration of various molecules was an incidental occurrence. As
our work has progressed, many other questions have arisen and so
fascinating has become the study, and so wide its ramifications

into all fields of biological endeavours, that it was decided to piece together our findings in this monograph. To permit consecutive reading, the various chapters follow the same course as our investigations and each is sufficiently detailed to include all the important findings. This has been done to allow readers and my friends of various scientific disciplines, some of whom are now actively engaged in similar work, to follow the logic behind the various moves and hypotheses we have made.

I express my thanks to my colleagues in the department of Bacteriology; to Dr. R. Bather of the Saskatchewan Cancer Research Institute for his help with our animal cell work; to Mr. Ronald Hodges and Miss Janet Walker for very able technical assistance, to my graduate students, to Mrs. Marjorie Gibson for her patience during the typing and preparation of the scripts, and to the Defence Research Board of Canada for financing the work.

S. J. W.

# CONTENTS

# Bound Water
## in
# Biological Integrity

# CHAPTER 1

# BOUND WATER AND THE SURVIVAL OF MICROBES

## Introduction and Methods

W E COMMENCED OUR WORK with a study of the effect of desiccation on the death rates of selected species of bacteria. The major problem was how to dry these cells and, at the same time, accurately control their water content. A technique was required that would allow the rapid removal of unwanted water but desiccation on filters or in vials did not seem, at the time, too satisfactory. Since it was considered necessary to disperse the cells as much as possible, to avoid the complication of one cell protecting another, by cell to cell contact, the answer seemed to lie in the use of an aerosol. The literature was surveyed, therefore, for information as to the behaviour of air-borne cells and the techniques employed in such studies. The latter proved to be numerous and often extremely complex, however, the author was fortunate to learn of a relatively simple apparatus designed by Dr. L. Goldberg at the University of California. A description of this equipment was subsequently published in 1958. It consisted of a rotating drum into which cells could be atomized by a collison spray (Henderson, 1952), the unique part of the apparatus was its ability to rotate at a constant speed. This minimized the physical "fall out" of the air-borne particles. Both the collison spray and the rotating drum were adopted by our laboratories although the design of our drum differed slightly from that of Goldbergs. Our drum was not a toroid but a cylinder with stainless steel sides four feet in diameter separated by a plastic wall two feet in width. As it was intended to study also the effects of light the plastic chosen transmitted wavelengths above 2800A and in a second all steel drum lights were actually fixed inside.

The collison spray generates droplets of 10 micron mean diameter and was operated at 28 psi. Air cleaned by passage through spin filters and charcoal and dried in a column of silica gel was used to operate the spray. Samples were taken from the aerosol with a liquid impinger operating at 12.5 litres/min: by means of a critical orifice. Both drums were mounted in a Dexion frame on wheels allowing either drum to be placed in various refrigerated or x-ray rooms (Figs. 1-1 and 1-1a).

Figure 1-1 End view of the stainless steel drum showing the all glass impinger on the right and spraying apparatus on the left of the main central shaft.

The literature survey revealed that most of the work conducted with airborne microbes had concerned itself with attempts to explain airborne infections. Studies on the transmission of infection through the air at a distance greater than that envisaged

Figure 1-1a Side view of the drum showing humidity gauge, air-drier, filter and spray.

under the term "droplet infection" have been made for many years and these became the subject of reviews by Buchbinder (1942) and Robertson (1943). Before these reviews appeared, however, Wells and his colleagues were studying experimental aerosols of bacteria and in 1937 they reported that temperature and humidity affected the longevity of airborne microbes and that the effect varied with the bacterial species. This observation stimulated studies on the effect of the atmospheric environment on airborne cells. In 1942, Williamson and Gotaas and, in 1944, DeOme reported that the death rate of bacteria rose with increasing humidity and Loosli *et al.* (1943) reported similar findings with influenza virus. Wells and Zapposodi (1948), however, found death rates to be higher at low humidity. By studying the dissappearance of methylene blue from aerosols, Dunklin and Puck (1948) attempted to distinguish between apparent and real decrease in the viability of *Streptococcus haemolyticus* aerosols due respectively to settling and death. These authors subsequently reported that death rates were maximal between 50 and 60 per cent relative humidity (RH) and that deaths occurred in two stages, a period of rapid death, taking place during the first fifteen minutes, and a later period of slower death. These secondary deaths were so small that estimates of deaths above or below 60 per cent RH sometimes appeared as negative values. The authors stated, however, that this critical RH level could not be detected if salt was omitted from the aerosolising medium. They thus assumed death to be due to rapid osmotic pressure changes in the drying drop and that at 60 per cent RH the cellular water was saturated with solutes.

In 1947, Rosebury published a monograph on the effects of RH on airborne cells of *Pasteurella tularensis* and several other pathogens. Rosebury stated that while most of the organisms studied seemed to be more stable at 70-80 per cent RH and above, at lower RH ranges all were subject to destruction through mechanisms that remained obscure. The addition of dextrin or gelatin to the suspending medium improved the stability. Schechmeister and Goldberg, working with influenza virus reported in 1950 that this organism was more stable at 60 per cent

RH, and Ferry and Maple in 1954 reported the same critical RH level for *Micrococcus candidus*, but in later work (1958), using an electronic method of calculating cell numbers in an aerosol by light scatter, they observed no intermediate critical RH region. Wells, in 1955, published a review on airborne infection in which he summed up the situation to date. It appeared that no general agreement could be found between workers on the effects of RH or temperature. Mechanisms of oxidation of cellular protein; the buildup of toxic metabolites by slow metabolism, and osmotic pressure effects had been postulated as the reasons for death in the drying drops.

The electronic counting device of Ferry *et al.* could only be used with aerosols generated from distilled water, since the addition of solids to the spray suspension produced droplet nuclei which did not contain bacterial cells, and these interfered with the calculations of cell numbers.

Radioactive compounds have been used extensively to study cellular metabolism and in 1952, Harper and Morton reported that they were able to determine the distribution in the animal body of *Bacillus subtilis* spores by using spores labelled with phosphorus 32 ($P^{32}$). It seemed to the author that cells labelled with $P^{32}$ might well be valuable as tracers in an aerosol and enable total cell numbers to be counted. The same notion had occurred to Harper *et al.*, for in 1958 they reported the use of these spores as tracers in experimental aerosols. These authors reported that the spores did not seem to be a reliable tracer and stated that vegetative cells of the test organism labelled with $P^{32}$ and killed with formalin were better. A similar technique was reported by the author (Webb, 1957), using radioactive tracer cells of the organisms obtained by growth in a liquid medium containing $P^{32}$ and subsequently killed with iodine. Since the phosphorus did not leach from the cells during aerosolization and collection reliable results were obtained using these tracer cells.

It was considered that by the use of the tracer techniques some of the difficulties encountered by previous workers would be overcome and more exact studies of biological aerosols made possible. In view of the varying opinions as to the cause of death, and the apparent lack of agreement between workers on environmental effects, the author decided that initial studies should be carried out on the survival of airborne organisms atomized from distilled water. Further, the effect of substances added to the spray suspension also needed to be determined. This latter topic has hitherto not been studied, except for a mention by Rosebury (1947), and it seemed to the author that this might be a major factor influencing survival.

Throughout the initial studies in our laboratories a single method of culturing and preparing the cells for aerosolization was used. Initially dead radioactive cells in equal quantity to live cells were added to check the physical settling rate of the airborne cells, however, this procedure was discontinued when it became clear that "fall out" was small and extremely constant. The settling rate was checked when the organism or spray medium was changed. All of the bacteria were cultured in 2 per cent Bacto Tryptose plus 1 per cent Glucose on a rotary shaker at 30°C. The cells from 20ml. apiquots of a twenty-four hour culture were harvested by centrifugation at 8000 rpm., washed twice in distilled de-ionized water and finally re-suspended in 20 ml. of de-ionized water. This final suspension was then atomized into the drum. Collection from the aerosol was carried out for one minute in 10.0 ml. of 0.85 per cent NaCl (Saline), (Webb 1959).

**The Effect of Relative Humidity**

The results of initial studies at 50 per cent RH with four different bacteria (Fig. 1-2) demonstrated that up to 50 per cent of the cells of a sensitive organism such as *Serratia marcesens* are killed during the five minutes required to generate the aerosol and take the first sample. The rate at which these early deaths took place agreed favourably with the results of Ferry *et al.* (1958). Since no loss of viability occurred in the cells remaining in the spray bottle after the aerosol had been generated these early deaths appeared to result from damage caused by the first stages of drying. The findings of Wells (1955) that $10\mu$ drops even when suspended in air of 80 per cent RH evaporated in microseconds make the above assumption not unreasonable. Also, some experi-

ments with dynamic aerosols stored for up to fifteen seconds support such an argument (Webb 1960). However, our main interest
was centered around the happenings in an established aerosol
over at least thirty minutes and since the established average
aerosol contains from 1 to 2 x $10^7$ cells/litre of air and viability
losses of up to four orders of magnitude were encountered, the
loss at the beginning of 50 per cent of the cells did not affect our
experiments. In fact, in later work, the number of these early
deaths helped to formulate a working hypothesis as to the cause of
death.

The published data of other workers, in the main, are expressed
in terms of first order kinetics, and often only the death rate
constants (k), calculated from plots of $lnN_t/N_0$ against time, are
quoted. Our results, shown in Fig. 1-2, show that over a full five-
hour period at 50 per cent RH, first order kinetics do not hold.
However, if only the first hour is considered, a straight line relationship fits the data well (Fig. 1-2: dotted line). Since most
of the previous work had been conducted on periods of less than
one hour it was decided to present our results in terms of two
death rates, $K_1$ for the period up to one hour and $K_2$ for the
period one to five hours. This made it possible to compare our
data with that of other workers and so determine the effect of
environmental changes on the two time intervals. It also considerably simplified the presentation of results.

The death rates calculated were in good agreement with those
of Ferry *et al.* (1958), who had studied cells aerosolized from
water. Their K values were 0.021 and 0.042 for *E coli* and *S
marcescens* respectively, and ours were 0.029 and 0.036 min$^{-1}$. In
contrast to these high values, the death rate of *Staph. albus* was
only 0.006. These preliminary runs were then followed by a series
of experiments designed to examine the effect of RH from which
a constant pattern of cell behavior was evident. At relative humidities above 70 per cent, very few cell deaths occurred in any of the
organisms studied, then as the RH was lowered between 70 per
cent and 30 per cent RH, a rapid decline in their stability took
place. The only exception seemed to be *Staph. albus* which retained its viability extremely well at all RH levels tested and later

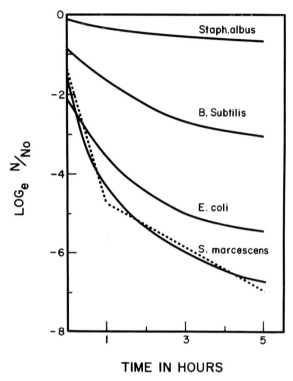

Figure 1-2 The effect of aerosolization at 50 per cent RH on the viability of several species of bacteria. The dotted lines are the two time periods chosen and the slope of each represents 0·1 hour $= K_1$, 1·5 hours $= K_2$ (taken from Webb, *Canad. J. Microbiol.*, 5, 1959) .

work with *Staph. aureus* showed this organism to be even hardier. A second finding was that while the maximal rate of increase in $K_1$ values occurred between 70 and 50 per cent RH, that of the $K_2$ values occurred between 50 and 40 per cent RH. Thus at 30 per cent RH, $K_1$ and $K_2$ had approximately the same value and the function $K = 1/t \ln N_t/N_o$ applied throughout the entire five-hour period of aerosolization. The results shown in Fig. 1-3 for *Serratia marcescens* and *Staph albus* are typical of those obtained with sensitive and resistant organisms respectively. (The absolute death rates of sensitive organisms differed slightly.) All of the gram negative organisms studied, which included various species of *Pseudomonas; Escherichia, Serratia, Proteus* and *Neisseria,* were highly sensitive to aerosolization and, although their individual death rates differed slightly, the changes in $K_1$ and $K_2$ values with respect to RH were the same.

It was clear that the ability of a cell to withstand desiccation in aerosols was an intrinsic property of the cell. However, the constant pattern in the response of unstable cells to changes in RH was more meaningful. It suggested that the reason for instability was common to many different genera and was related in some way to the water content of the cell.

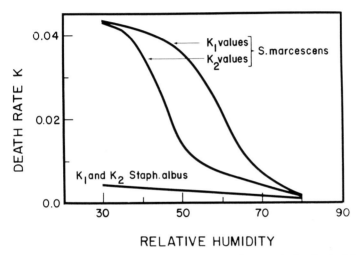

RELATIVE HUMIDITY

Figure 1-3 The effect of relative humidity on the survival of air-dried *S. marcescens* and *Staph. aureus.* $K_1 =$ the death rate during the first hour. $K_2 =$ the death rate during the next four hours.

## Bound Water Content and Cell Death

At the time, there was no way of measuring the water content of the cells in aerosols so it became necessary to utilize a film drying technique. The cell suspensions were prepared in exactly the same way as for the aerosol, but instead of being aerosolized, from 100 to 200 mg. wet weight of cells were deposited on 4" dia. millipore filters. Portions of the films containing from 1 to 10 mg. wet weight of cells were then transferred in small aluminum planchets to the pan of a microbalance housed in a cabinet in which both temperature and humidity could be controlled. The rate of water loss was determined and the equilibrium water content calculated by drying the films at 110°C. after no further loss could be detected in humidity cabinet. Under these conditions the rate of water loss was considerably slower than in the aerosol, but provided the films were kept thin the evaporation rate followed a definite pattern. In later experiments, measurements of the amount of light scattered by a given number of water atomized airborne cells were utilized to measure the refractive index of the airborne cells at various levels of RH and the water content estimated from the changes in refractive index. The formula for this is described in chapter two. Although a greater error was encountered, the water contents calculated agreed favourably with those found on filters. If the water content was expressed in terms of gms of water/100 gms. of cell solids, as has been customary in other publications, the evaporation rate on the filters remained constant down to about 80 gms. $H_2O$/100 gms. protein but increased as further water was withdrawn. The calculated values at 25°C and 30 per cent RH were down to 80 gms., 0.082; 80-40 gms., 0.10; 40-20 gms., 0.13; 20-5 gms. 0.14. Although these ranges of water content were arbitrarily chosen, this observation demonstrated that as water was withdrawn from the cell it became successively easier to remove the remainder. A simple statement, but when considered with the equilibrium water content of the cells at various RH levels, its meaning became more significant.

The results of the water content measurements on cells of *S. marcescens* are shown in Fig. 1-4, with the spread of the death rates (K) indicated by the vertical arrows. It is evident that even at 90 per cent RH the cells lose considerable water, yet the death rate is negligible. The cells of *S. marcescens*, as will be shown later in this monograph, consist of about 80 per cent water and 20 per cent solids, therefore, 100 gms. of cell solids would normally have some 400 gms. of water associated with it. These two facts demonstrate clearly that up to 90 per cent of the cell's water can be removed without it being damaged. Apparently, cell death only occurs when the water content is lowered to about 30 gms.

$H_2O/100$ gms. of cell solids and then the death rate increases rapidly as the water content, at equilibrium, falls below this level. The water content curve in Fig. 1-4 is very similar to those reported by Bull (1944) for egg albumin and collagen and Scott (1958) for *Salmonella newport*. These authors reported that at 80 per cent RH approximately 32 gms. of water were present per 100 gms. of protein at equilibrium. At 60 per cent RH the reported water values per 100 gms. were; collagen, 20 gms.; Egg albumin, 12 gms.; *Salmonella* 15 gms. The value of 20 gms. for *S. marcescens* in our studies agreed favourably with these results. As it has been abundantly shown that proteins contain up to 40 gms. $H_2O/100$ gms. protein in the bound form (Edsall 1953; Low 1953), the above findings as to the amount of water involved made it clear that only the bound water was concerned in the mechanism by which cells died when desiccated. It was now understood why the water from 40 gm./100 gms. of cell solids downwards was more quickly removed than the bulk of the cell water. Presumably this water existed in the cell as a monolayer or partial monolayer and, as such, its removal would not be hindered by the presence of other water molecules.

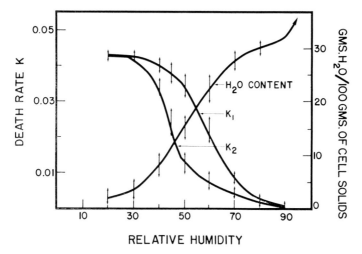

RELATIVE HUMIDITY

Figure 1-4 The effect of relative humidity on the water content and death rates of *S. marcescens*. (The vertical lines indicate the spread of these quantities found during many separate determinations).

The evidence so far obtained had demonstrated (a) that the removal of bound water led to the death of a cell, and (b) the aerosol was an excellent tool for studying the effect of changes in the bound water content of a cell on its reaction to other environmental conditions.

## The Effect of Temperature and Energy Relationships

Unfortunately, because facilities were not available by which temperatures above 25°C could be maintained, only a study of lower temperatures was possible. Initially a relative humidity of 30 per cent was used, since first order kinetics had been shown to apply over the full five hours at this level of RH. However, as the temperature was lowered $K_1$ and $K_2$ separated and the plot ln $N_t/N_o$ vs time became two phased. This simulated the findings at higher humidities although the difference between $K_1$ and $K_2$ was not as great (Webb 1959). The fact that an increase in temperature changed a biliniar graph into an exponential one suggested that the death of a cell resulted from one of at least two reactions. Also, since a lowering of the RH did the same, both reactions must involve bound water.

Apart from the determination of the type of curve and the estimation of death rate, the plots of ln $N_t/N_o$ vs. time had no other value. It was considered useful, therefore, at this stage, to look at the energies associated with reactions responsible for cell deaths which required a thermodynamic analysis of the results. A great deal of criticism has been leveled at the use of thermodynamic studies in biological investigations, most of the critics insisting that the reaction being studied is usually not an isolated system. However, there is no doubt that studies of this kind have yielded valuable information in enzymology, virology and biochemistry in general. It is true that the application of thermodynamic principles to biological experiments cannot be as exact as in pure physical chemistry until systems are better understood. However, they can be used in biology on a comparative basis, to indicate the nature of reactions in relation to one another and to others of a more defined nature.

The studies reported were viewed critically in order to determine whether a thermodynamic analysis of the results would yield any useful information. The kinetics of denaturations and inactivations have been reviewed by Neurath *et al.* (1944) who found that deviations from first order kinetics occurred in about one third of the studies. Critical analysis showed also that there were few kinetic studies with highly purified proteins and it is well known that impurities may affect even the order of the reaction. In more recent studies with purer proteins, some denaturations have appeared to follow first order kinetics (Kunitz, 1948; Levy and Benaglia, 1950; Haurowitz *et al.* 1952), some second order (Briggs and Hall, 1945), and others partial order (Lauffer and Carnelly, 1945), while in some cases the apparent order depended on the method of estimating the velocity (Putnam, 1953). This is a clear indication that there are numerous stages in protein denaturation. Where biological activity or function is used as the basis of determining rates, the possible reversal of some inactivations must be taken into account and it should also be realised that loss of activity may consist of a series of concomitant or consecutive changes, any one of which may produce inactivity and thus determine velocity. It is evident then that any quantity measured experimentally is a property of one or more reactions and constitutes the sum total of all effects.

Reviewing the first order graphs of $\ln N_t/N_o$ against time, it was considered that if the one to five hour period of death was isolated from the zero to one hour period a straight line was also a good fit to the experimental points, and at certain humidity and temperature levels the graphs were all definitely first order. In view of the very minor deviation from a first order graph at 30 per cent RH and below 20°C, and by the obvious divergence from true first order kinetics evident in numerous publications, it was considered that useful information could be obtained by treating each of the periods of death by first order kinetics and analysing them thermodynamically. This would permit a comparison between the two death periods and reveal any differences, and also allow the results to be compared with those of other workers.

In Fig. 1-5 the effect of temperature on $K_1$ and $K_2$ is shown in

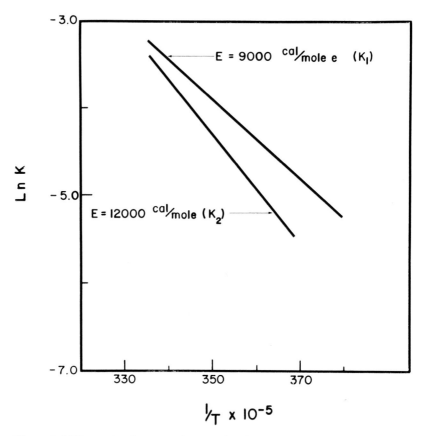

Figure 1-5 The activation energies associated with the death of air-borne *S. marcescens* at 30 per cent RH during the two experimental periods of 0-1 hour ($K_1$) and 1-5 hours ($K_2$) taken from Webb, *Canad. J. Microbiol., 5,* 1959).

typical Arrhenius fashion, lnK being plotted against the recipro-cal of the absolute temperature. The data are essentially those published in 1959 (Webb) with a few more recently determined death rates added. These additional K values, however, have not altered the published activation energies (E) calculated from the slope of the lines. The activation energy associated with the cell death appears to increase as the time of storage in air lengthens. Also, with temperature rise, $K_2$ increases more rapidly than $K_1$.

To decide on the meaning of these results it was necessary to consider them along with the observed effects of RH and the knowledge that an equilibrium between the bound water of the cell and the environmental water vapour is reached very quickly. It was clear that the rate of cell death was controlled by the amount of bound water remaining at equilibrium and that this amount was determined by either RH or temperature. The mere removal of the water molecules themselves should not kill a cell so presumably death was a result of a process made possible by the loss of water. As the only likely process seemed to be a structural change in a vital macromolecule, the number of structural water molecules present was considered to control the ease with which the dehydrated or semi-dehydrated groups of the macromolecule could interact. This would then determine the death rate. The calculated E. values, therefore, were thought to represent the strengths and/or number of new inter or intra-molecular H-bonds formed when the remaining water molecules re-orientated themselves or dehydrated groups interacted. The probability of such a change, and of it being lethal to a cell, was considered to depend on the spacial arrangements of the groups of the macromolecule as well as the flexibility of its "backbone" structure. It followed, therefore, that the greater the distortion the higher the E values should become. To examine this hypothesis the entropy ($\Delta S$) changes associated with both periods of storage in air were calculated from equation 1.

*Equation 1*

$$K = \frac{K_b}{h} e^{\Delta S/R} e^{-\Delta H/RT}$$

Where K $=$ Death rate of cells
K$_b$     Boltzmann's constant
h      Plank's constant
T      Absolute temperature
$\Delta$S      Activation entropy
$\Delta$H*      Heat of Activation
R      Gas constant in Cal/mole
$\Delta$H* was assumed equal to E (Putnam 1953)

*Bound Water in Biological Integrity*

The negative entropy of aerosol death indicated that the process of death involved a tightening of molecules. Since the removal of water in itself should result in a positive entropy change
it was of interest to compare the activation entropies calculated
with those of other workers. Pollard and Reaume (1951), and
Pollard and Dimond (1953) have studied the inactivation of
several viruses in wet and dry states and their results are compared
with those from our studies in Table 1-I.

TABLE 1-I
ACTIVATION ENERGIES AND ENTROPIES
FOR THE INACTIVATION OF MICRO-ORGANISMS

| Organism | Condition | $E (\Delta H)$ cal/mole | $\Delta S$ | Reference |
|---|---|---|---|---|
| T-1 phage | dry | 27,500 | 0 | Pollard & Reaume (1951) |
| | wet | 95,000 | 207 | |
| T-2 phage | dry | 18,000 | −12 | Pollard & Reaume (1951) |
| | wet | 71,000 | 139 | |
| T-3 phage | dry | 19,100 | − 9 | Pollard & Reaume (1951) |
| | wet | 105,000 | 246 | |
| T-7 phage | dry | 12,700 | −29 | |
| *TMV | dry | 27,000 | 0 | Pollard & Dimond (1953) |
| †SBMV | dry | 17,000 | −16 | Pollard & Dimond (1953) |
| S. marcescens | aerosol $(K_1)$ | 9,000 | −40 | Webb (1961) |
| | aerosol $(K_2)$ | 12,000 | −18 | |
| E. coli | areosol $(K_1)$ | 8,500 | −38 | Webb (1961) |
| | aerosol $(K_2)$ | 10,000 | −19 | |
| Rous Sarcoma virus | aerosol $(K_1)$ | 12,000 | −16 | Webb (1961) |
| | areosol $(K_2)$ | 15,000 | − 9 | |

*Tobacco mosaic virus.
†Southern bean mosaic virus.

From this comparison, the most striking point is that the
values of E are much smaller, and the values of $\Delta S$ negative when
micro-organisms are inactivated in the dry state. Pollard (1953)
points out that the entropy change does not seem to be related to
the size of the organism, which suggests that inactivation takes
place in relatively small regions of the cell and is indicative of
specialised molecular structure and function in the cells. It was
evident too, that the values of E and $\Delta S$ for aerosol death were of
the same order as those reported for the inactivation of dried
viruses.

Therefore, we examined the effect of RH and temperature on Rous sarcoma and Pigeon pox viruses in aerosols. The latter virus was found to be extremely hardy and under our experimental conditions no inactivation was found. Rous sarcoma on the other hand was very sensitive to RH changes and displayed the same pattern of behaviour as bacteria. At relative humidities above 70 per cent, the inactivation rates were negligible but they increased rapidly as the RH was lowered below this level (Webb, Bather and Hodges, 1963). Also, the same bilinear relationship between ln $N_t/N_o$ and time were observed at intermediate RH levels around 50 per cent (Fig. 1-6).

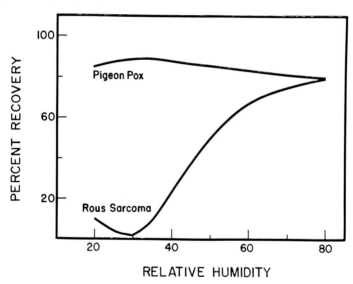

Figure 1-6 The effect of relative humidity on air-borne Pigeon Pox and Rous Sarcoma viruses (taken from Webb, Bather and Hodges, *Canad. J. Microbiol.*, *9*, 1963).

The magnitudes of E and Δ S indicated that the changes taking place in the cell and which led to its death were of a subtle nature. The denaturation of most proteins by heat involve values of E of over 160,000 cal. mole and entropy changes of around 300 entropy units (E.U.). Even though the measured values for bacterial death must be considered the result of the sum of more than one reaction, this total is small since Neurath *et al.* (1942) has estimated that an increase of 100 E.U. corresponds to a change of only 0.5 per cent in the vibrational frequency for a molecule with 10,000 internal degrees of freedom. However, most of the heat inactivations have been carried out at relatively high temperatures in the range, 60-80°C, and it has been shown by Cherry and Watson (1949) that E and Δ S can be a function of the temperature range studied. Pollard (1953) also found that the wet heat inactivation of *Tobacco mosaic virus* yielded two sets of figures: below 85°C E was 40,000 and Δ S 18 and above 85°C E was 195,000 and Δ S 410 E.U. This indicates that two very different processes are involved in denaturation at low and high temperatures. It is possible, therefore, that the difference between the E and Δ S values of inactivations of wet and dry cells at low temperatures is due to the relative amounts of water in the cell. Thus the positive Δ S and higher E values of wet inactivations is due to the necessity of removing considerably more water molecules from sites on the protein. Naturally, if there were several water layers covering one site, a possible attack on the vital site would be more difficult than if no such protective layer existed. This in itself speaks strongly for the stabilising action of water in molecular structure.

**The Combined Effect of Temperature and Relative Humidity**

When organisms are aerosolised from distilled water it is clear that both temperature and RH profoundly affect their behaviour. It was reasonable then to assume that these two factors must interact with one another and in an attempt to examine this interaction, several formulae relating vapour pressure and temperature were examined with little success until a formula relating the evaporation rate of water droplets with temperature was employed. The starting formula was that developed by Frossling:—

$$-\frac{dm}{dt} = A \quad \frac{(Po\text{-}P)}{T} \quad (2)$$

where A is a constant which includes such things as a diffusion constant of vapour, and the gas constant R; Po and P are the

saturated pressures and partial pressures of water vapour at temp
$T$ (°A)., then since $RH = \dfrac{100\,P}{Po}$

$$Po\text{-}P = Po\,\dfrac{(1\text{-}RH)}{100}$$

and $-\dfrac{dm}{dt} = A\,\dfrac{Po}{T}\,(100 - RH)$   (3)

The death rates $K_1$ and $K_2$ obtained at different values of $T$
and RH were then plotted against the function $\dfrac{Po}{T}\,(100\ RH)$ and
the results of such plots, shown in Fig. 1-7, indicated that the
death rate could be correlated with the evaporation rate of water.
The type of plot obtained was sigmoidal but there was considerable spread of the points at values of the function $\dfrac{Po}{T}\,(100 - RH)$

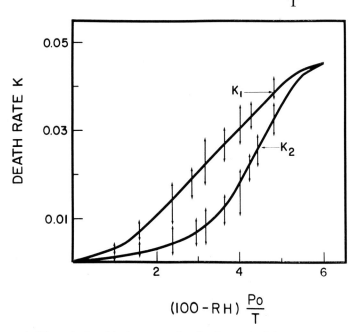

$$(100 - RH)\ \frac{Po}{T}$$

Figure 1-7 The relationship between the death rates of *S. marcescens* during
the 0-1 hour $(K_1)$ and 1-5 hour $(K_2)$ periods of aerosolization and the
function (100-RH) Po/T derived from an equation describing the evaporation rate of water droplets at different temperatures (Frossling, 1938) (taken
from Webb, *Canad. J. Microbiol., 9,* 1959) .

(function f) around two. Low values of f are obtained under conditions of low temperature or high humidity, thus it appeared that at these low f values the death rate of cells was more a function of temperature than humidity and hence the spread in points. It was evident too that there was a difference between $K_1$ and $K_2$ with respect to this function for a straight line relationship between $K_1$ and values of f between two and five appeared to exist, whereas this relationship for $K_2$ only existed between f values of three to five.

It was gratifying to obtain a mathematical function by which the death rate of cells could be predicted over a fairly wide range of RH and temperature values, but it is never too satisfactory to have just an empirical formula without knowing what it means. Therefore, we viewed these graphs in the light of the evidence we had obtained earlier. It was clear that all evaporation, as far as free water was concerned, took place almost instantaneously on aerosolisation and, therefore, function f could not represent water evaporation as such. Also, the $\Delta S$ and E values associated with the reactions responsible for death indicated a union of molecules or chemical groups rather than their separation, and that this union was associated with a relatively constant but small amount of energy.

The sigmoidal nature and similarity of the curves obtained when K values were plotted against the bound water content of cells or function f, suggested to us that this latter function reflected the quantity of water remaining in the cell at equilibrium and presumably represented the rate at which $H_2O$ molecules bound to the chemical groups of macromolecules exchanged with the environmental water vapour. These exchange rates would then determine the quantity of water adsorbed at any given time. In other words, function f appeared to be related to the exchange rates of gases associated with adsorption isotherm calculations.

Since the adsorption of gases follows various patterns according to the system studied, it appeared more than a coincidence that the sigmoid curve obtained in plots of cell bound water content vs. RH and death rate K vs. function f displayed the same characteristics as the adsorption of water to such chemicals as charcoal (Glasstone, 1950). This type of adsorption pattern is generally associated with Van der Waals forces and is characterised by relatively small E values of 5K cal.mole or less. Also, it can be described by the equation:—

$$\frac{P/Po}{v\,(1\text{-}P/Po)} = \frac{1}{v_m C} + \frac{(C\text{-}1)}{v_m C}\,P/Po$$

where $v_m$ = amount adsorbed when monolayer formed.
$v$ = amount adsorbed in experiment
$C = e^{(E - E_1)\,RT}$

from which it is clear that v, the amount of gas adsorped is proportional to $(100 - RH)$ and hence to function f. The incorporation of temperature effects, however, makes the physico-chemical calculations relatively complex, especially since the nature of the surface on which the adsorption takes place will influence any mathematical description of the process. It was considered unnecessary, therefore, to delve too deeply into the mathematical descriptions of microbial death, the shape of the water vapour adsorption isotherms, the bound water vs. RH and function f or RH vs. cell death rate curves all displayed the same pattern and thus it appeared evident that the death rate was directly related to the amount of bound water remaining in a cell at equilibrium. It merely remained necessary to measure the water content of cells at various RH values and temperatures below 25°C. and plot death rates as a function of water content. These results are shown in Fig. 1-8, from which it would appear that the deaths taking place during the first hour are associated with changes in the cell due to the loss of the first 15 gms. $H_2O/100$ gms. of cell solids and those in the later period with the loss of a further 10 gms. $H_2O$.

Throughout these experiments, the temperature of the liquid impinger had been kept constant at 25°C. but the possibility existed that some of the deaths might be due to rehydration in the impinger. It seemed unlikely that all of the deaths were due to such a phenomenon since, if they had been, the number of deaths would have remained constant with the time of aerosolization. However, to check the magnitude of rehydration kill the airborne cells were collected at different temperatures in the liquid im-

pinger and by a dry Anderson sampler utilizing direct impinge-
ment on a solid medium in a Petri dish or collection on millipore
filters. The filters were then placed on nutrient media and
colonies allowed to develop. Differences in the recoveries of viable
cells from aerosols held at 30 per cent RH by the various methods
were encountered but they were no greater than a factor of two
to three. Only in one instance was a large difference found and
this was when the cells on millipore filters were allowed to re-
hydrate slowly from 30 per cent RH to 90 per cent RH before
being placed on the agar medium. Apparently, slow rehydration
from 30 per cent RH to 90 per cent RH resulted in the death of a
further 90 per cent of the surviving cells. The significance of this
was not immediately apparent but became clearer as the work
progressed and is discussed in chapter six. At the time, it did con-
firm the results of various other workers regarding controlled rehydration of micro-organisms after drying. It seemed fairly clear
that the observed deaths amounting to as much as three to four
orders of magnitude were a direct result of a process occurring in
the aerosol and not one due to the spraying or collection.

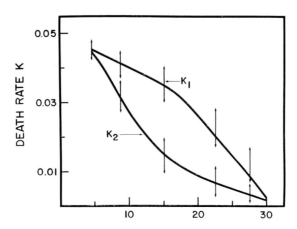

H$_2$O CONTENT GMS/IOO GMS CELL SOLIDS

Figure 1-8 The effect of the bound water content of *S. marcescens* on the
death rate of cells during the 0-1 hour (K$_1$) and 1-5 hour (K$_2$) periods of
aerosolization. The vertical lines represent the spread in the death rates
found during at least twenty separate experiments.

## Summary and Conclusions

In any macromolecule, there are many molecular configurations possible and it seemed reasonable to conclude that some of these rely on correctly placed water molecules. If this is true, then obviously the removal of these water molecules will result in the formation of a new structure which may or may not be lethal to the cell. Presumably the more water molecules removed, the larger become the possible lethal changes either by re-orientation of other $H_2O$ molecules, or by the formation of inter or intra molecular bonds.

The results of these studies with air-borne cells atomized from distilled water suggested that the death rate was dependent upon the level of bound water molecules remaining in the cell when the cell reached an equilibrium with the environmental water vapour. The small energies associated with the mechanism responsible for death, and the apparent increase in entropy both indicated a subtle change involving the formation of new bonds. However, it was apparent that deaths took place in at least two phases, one associated with the loss of water fairly weakly held by the cell components, and the other with more firmly held water. This was suggested by the difference in the response of the death rates to RH and temperature during the two time periods studied.

Therefore, it seemed reasonable to suppose that death was the result of interactions between such groups as $-OH$, $-NH$, $=C=O$ or $=P=O$ when water hydrogen bonded to them was removed. The strength with which these groups hold water molecules varies and the assumption was made that this phenomenon was responsible for the apparent two phased death rate versus time curve obtained at 50 per cent RH. From such an hypothesis, it follows that the water bonded to $-N$, $=N-H$ or $-OH$ groups would be removed first and some cells would die while others would survive, depending on the particular new molecular structures formed. On further desiccation at higher temperatures or lower humidities, the water held by $=C=O$ or $=P=O$ would be removed and produce an increase in the death rate during the $K_2$ period. The group interactions could of course be intra or intermolecular, and whether or not particular ones took place would undoubtedly depend on the temperature and the velocity at which the bound water molecules exchanged with those of the environment. This latter assumption may explain why many cells survive vacuum freeze drying, presumably the low temperatures will not allow violent distortions of the molecules and hence increase the chances that the new bonds made will be either reversible with water or non-lethal. It is more probable that at these low temperatures much of the bound water is left intact. Scott (1957) working with freeze dried cells has stated that the removal of the most firmly held water appears to result in viability loss.

Our studies with cells dried from distilled water ended temporarily with this idea in mind, and we turned our attention to the effect of inert gases or chemicals on the response of cells to changes in relative humidity.

# CHAPTER 2

# THE INFLUENCE OF ADDED CHEMICALS ON BOUND WATER AND CELL SURVIVAL

## The Effect of Added Proteins, Peptides and Amino Acids

AT THIS STAGE OF THE INVESTIGATIONS, no intermediate conditions of RH and temperature had been found to be optimal for cellular aerosol death, and it was felt that these optima, observed by other workers, could have been due to the effects of the constituents of the medium from which the cells had been aerosolised. Rosebury (1947) stated that dextrin and gelatin, when added to the spray medium, afforded some stability to the airborne cells, and Morton (1958) observed that cells, aerosolised from a casein digest medium, were more stable in air than cells atomised from water. In view of these reports, the effect of casein digest, and various sugars on the death of the air-borne cells were studied.

When cells were aerosolised from a 5 per cent solution of casein acid digest extremely rapid death occurred, and all cells were dead within one hour of air suspension. This result was very different from that reported by Morton (1958). However, when a tryptic digest was used, the cells were more air stable, but only at RH levels of 50 per cent or more. There seemed to be two possible explanations of this result, (a) that the large amount of NaCl present in the neutralised acid hydrolysate was toxic, and (b) that the milder tryptic hydrolysis produced protective compounds.

It was decided, therefore, to carry out controlled acid hydrolyses of two proteins and to neutralise the hydrolysates by the method of Buc *et al.* (1945), which is based on the fact that monocarboxylic-monoamino acids are not adsorbed by acid bind-

27

ing resins of the weak base type. Sheehan *et al.* (1950) used it
successfully to remove acid from hydrolysates. The hydrolysis was
carried out on 10 per cent suspensions of casein and haemoglobin
using 6N HCl. At various times 50 ml. aliquots were removed
and neutralised by passage through a glass column containing
the ion exchange resin Amberlite IR4B. Twenty ml. of the neutralised effluent were used as a suspending fluid for the cells and
another 20 ml. was used for the formol titration of $\alpha$-amino nitrogen by the Sorensen method (Sahyun, 1948; Dawes, 1956). To
determine the degree of hydrolysis, 100 per cent hydrolysis was
taken as the point at which no further increase in $\alpha$-amino nitrogen was obtained by continued hydrolysis.

The results given in Table 2-I show that at 50 per cent RH and
above the death rate of cells at all periods of air storage became
higher as the amount of $\alpha$-amino nitrogen increased.

TABLE 2-I

THE EFFECT OF THE DEGREE OF HYDROLISIS OF CASEIN AND HAEMOGLOBIN ON THE
DEATH RATES OF *S. marcescens* AND *E. coli* AT 50% RH, 25°C.

| % Amino Nitrogen | | Death Rates | | | |
|---|---|---|---|---|---|
| | | $K_1 \, min^{-1}$ (0-1 hr) | | $K_2 \, min^{-1}$ (1-5 hr) | |
| | | A | B | A | B |
| Non-hydrolysed | (1) | 0.038 | 0.031 | 0.033 | 0.021 |
| Non-hydrolysed | (2) | 0.036 | 0.029 | 0.021 | 0.022 |
| 11.7 | (1) | 0.005 | 0.001 | 0.003 | 0.002 |
| 12.0 | (2) | 0.003 | 0.001 | 0.003 | 0.003 |
| 18.2 | (1) | 0.006 | 0.005 | 0.003 | 0.004 |
| 17.6 | (2) | 0.005 | 0.007 | 0.005 | 0.003 |
| 28.5 | (1) | 0.008 | 0.010 | 0.007 | 0.009 |
| 30.6 | (2) | 0.007 | 0.009 | 0.010 | 0.011 |
| 50.8 | (1) | 0.013 | 0.011 | 0.010 | 0.014 |
| 53.1 | (2) | 0.016 | 0.018 | 0.013 | 0.014 |
| 72.6 | (1) | 0.020 | 0.016 | 0.018 | 0.016 |
| 71.8 | (2) | 0.024 | 0.022 | 0.016 | 0.015 |
| 88.3 | (2) | 0.028 | 0.028 | 0.022 | 0.021 |
| 85.2 | (2) | 0.026 | 0.029 | 0.025 | 0.020 |
| 100.0 | (1) | 0.033 | 0.035 | 0.024 | 0.021 |
| 100.0 | (2) | 0.037 | 0.033 | 0.025 | 0.024 |
| Water suspension | | 0.036 | 0.031 | 0.022 | 0.025 |

A = *S. marcescens*                    1 = Casein
B = *E. coli*                          2 = Haemoglobin
Removal of acid by means of IRA4B.
Taken from Webb, S. J. *Canad. J. Microbiol.* 6, (1960a).

This suggested that either the first formed amino acids were
protective, or that protection was a function of the chain length
of the components of the protein hydrolysate. Because of the

amounts of compounds required in these experiments, it seemed useless to try and separate the components of the hydrolysate by electrophoresis or chemical precipitation; therefore, amino acids and other compounds of known composition were used to ascertain the effect of individual amino acids and their higher polymers. Since some of the amino acids were not too soluble in water, a strict comparison could not be made on a weight/volume basis. However, 5 per cent solutions were used except where the solubility of the compound made it impossible. In such cases, a saturated solution was employed and with native proteins a 5 per cent emulsion.

TABLE 2-II

THE EFFECT OF THE ADDITIONS TO THE SPRAY SUSPENSION ON THE DEATH RATES OF *S. marcescens* AEROSOLISED AT 50% RH AND 25°C.

| Compound Added | Concentration in Spray Suspension (%) | Death Rates $K_1$ (0-1 hr) | $K_2$ (1-5 hr) |
|---|---|---|---|
| None | | 0.036 | 0.022 |
| dl Alanine | 5 | 0.040 | 0.025 |
| Aspartic | Sat.* | 0.040 | 0.024 |
| Arginine | 5 | 0.022 | 0.014 |
| Amino butyric | 5 | 0.046 | 0.032 |
| dl Cysteine | 5 | 0.038 | 0.025 |
| Glycine | 5 | 0.020 | 0.014 |
| Hydroxyproline | 5 | 0.019 | 0.010 |
| Isoleucine | Sat. | 0.037 | 0.023 |
| Leucine | Sat. | 0.035 | 0.023 |
| Lycine | 5 | 0.024 | 0.018 |
| Methionine | Sat. | 0.036 | 0.021 |
| Ornithine | 5 | 0.021 | 0.016 |
| Phenylalanine | Sat. | 0.036 | 0.024 |
| dl Proline | 5 | 0.023 | 0.017 |
| Serine | 5 | 0.022 | 0.015 |
| Threonine | 5 | 0.025 | 0.017 |
| Tyrosine | Sat. | 0.038 | 0.021 |
| Valine | Sat. | 0.040 | 0.024 |
| Tryptic Casein Hydrolysate | 5 | 0.010 | 0.008 |
| Acid Casein Hydrolysate | 5 | 0.080 | — |
| Difco Yeast | 5 | 0.038 | 0.023 |
| Glutathione | 5 | 0.020 | 0.015 |
| Bacto Peptone | 5 | 0.013 | 0.010 |
| Bacto Proteose Peptone | 5 | 0.010 | 0.005 |
| Bacto Protone | 5 | 0.006 | 0.005 |
| Blood Albumin | 5† | 0.034 | 0.020 |
| Haemoglobin | 5† | 0.036 | 0.021 |
| Egg Albumin | 5† | 0.036 | 0.022 |

*Saturated solution.
†As emulsion.
The standard deviation for $K_1 = 0.0015$; $K_2 = 0.0008$.
*Taken from Webb, S. J., *Canad. J. Microbiol.* 6, (1960a).

The results of Table 2-II showed that all of the basic amino acids, the hydroxy amino acids, proline and glycine afforded the cells slight protection but greater protection was afforded by peptides used in the form of Bacto peptone, proteose-peptone and protone (rendered NaCl free by ion exchange on Amberlite IRC 50 and IR4B), while native proteins appeared to have no protective effect. From this it was apparent that the protective compounds in the protein hydrolysates were the peptones and proteoses and that amino acids containing a ketonic group, as suggested by amino butyric, were toxic.

When the effects of RH were studied, it was found that the protective ability of the peptides, proteoses and protones decreased as the RH was lowered and that at 30 per cent RH the slight protection afforded by these compounds was most apparent during the first hour. Large concentrations of Bacto protone were necessary to afford maximal protection and a 10 per cent concentration was used with varying quantities of NaCl in experiments designed to determine the effect of NaCl and other inorganic salts on the death of the air-borne cells. However, all the inorganic salts tested alone, with the exception of Sodium arsenite, proved to be extremely toxic during 0 to one hour periods and the death rates were so high that most of the cells were dead within an hour.

**The Effect of Salts**

The effects of RH on protone - NaCl aerosolised cells were quite different from those on protone or water atomised cells (Fig. 2-1). Maximum values of the death rates appeared, with NaCl at 0.1 - 0.7M, at 60 per cent RH, and at 0.7M NaCl a second peak in $K_2$ was observed at 30 per cent RH. The same peaks were observed with *E. coli* and *B. subtilis*, but NaCl caused no alteration of the effect of RH on *Staph. albus*. These results seemed to agree with those of Dunklin and Puck (1948), however, since the cells were more stable in concentrated solutions of protone than in water, it seemed reasonable to assume that the death of the cell was associated with cell structure rather than with osmotic effects and also that the protective action of some amino acids and peptides was due to their ability to maintain cell structure during periods of desiccation.

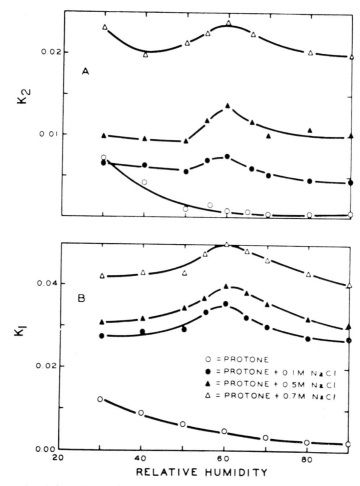

Figure 2-1 The effect of NaCl concentration on the death rates of *S. marcescens* aerosolized at various RH levels from a 10.0 per cent solution of Bacto-Protone. $K_1$ = death rate during the 0-1 hour period. $K_2$ = death rate during the 1-5 hour period (taken from Webb, *Canad. J. Microbiol., 6,* 1960).

The fact that all the chlorides tested affected the aerosols similarly was taken to indicate that the effects of NaCl were due to the Cl⁻ ion. The assumption that this ion inhibited the cellular protection of protone, and knowing that it would combine with the basic groups of this material, indicated that the basic groups of protone might be involved in the protective mechanism. Hence

it was deduced that the acidic groups of the cellular macromolecules might be associated with death. Nevertheless, the chloride
ion itself was also extremely toxic to the air-borne cells, indicating that its combination with the groups of cellular macromolecules induced death, suggesting the involvement also of basic
groups in the death mechanism. It, therefore, seemed possible
that the salt linkages were being destroyed by aerosolisation, but
it was difficult to visualise how this could be brought about by
the removal of cellular water and in view of the work described
in Chapter 1, the action of Cl⁻ ion was assumed to be due to its
ability to break the H-bonds between water and the -OH or -NH₂
groups of cellular constituents. Since sugars (Rosebury, 1947) had
been reported to afford stability to air-dried cells and these compounds do not possess -NH₂ groups, it seemed pertinent to conduct trials with alcohols and sugars.

TABLE 2-III

DEATH RATES OF *S. marcescens* AND *E. coli* AEROSOLISED FROM 10% SOLUTIONS OF
VARIOUS COMPOUNDS AT 50% RH AND 25°C.

| Compounds | Death Rates | | | |
|---|---|---|---|---|
| | $K_1$ (0-1 hr) | | $K_2$ (1-5 hr) | |
| | A | B | A | B |
| H₂O | 0.036 | 0.031 | 0.022 | 0.020 |
| Glycol | 0.080 | 0.091 | — | — |
| Glycerol | 0.064 | 0.066 | — | — |
| Erythritol | 0.032 | 0.035 | 0.019 | 0.020 |
| Xylose | 0.038 | 0.030 | 0.018 | 0.019 |
| Ribose | 0.039 | 0.040 | 0.015 | 0.019 |
| Glucose | 0.019 | 0.016 | 0.010 | 0.010 |
| Fructose | 0.028 | 0.019 | 0.010 | 0.010 |
| Mannose | 0.017 | 0.016 | 0.016 | 0.015 |
| Sorbose | 0.042 | 0.040 | 0.018 | 0.016 |
| Galactose | 0.028 | 0.016 | 0.013 | 0.011 |
| Dulcitol | 0.049 | 0.046 | 0.020 | 0.019 |
| Sucrose | 0.021 | 0.024 | 0.014 | 0.011 |
| Dextrin | 0.020 | 0.021 | 0.013 | 0.010 |
| Soluble Starch | 0.041 | 0.036 | 0.018 | 0.017 |

A = *S. marcescens*.
B = *E. coli*.
Taken from Webb, S. J., *Canad. J. Microbiol. 6*, 1960a) .

## The Effect of Polyalcohols, Sugars and Glucosamine

Cells of four organisms were aerosolised from 10 per cent
solutions of various hydroxy compounds and sugars at 50 per
cent RH, and as was observed with the amino acid polymers, the

effects on the cells in the aerosols seemed to depend on the chain length of the added compound (Table 2-III). While glycol and glycerol were extremely toxic, erythritol and the pentoses had no effect on the cells, but some hexoses, such as glucose and mannose, afforded some stability. The ketose sorbose did not protect, nor did the sugar alcohol dulcitol. Sucrose and dextrin afforded some protection but soluble starch did not.

It was evident, since the same weight-to-volume ratio had been used in all solutions, that the structure of the added compound was involved in its action on the bacterial cells. The fact that the ketose sugar and the sugar alcohol were slightly toxic, while the aldoses appeared protective, suggested that the carbonyl and primary alcohol groups might be toxic, and that the secondary alcohol groups protective. In view of this, and since at least a six carbon chain seemed necessary to confer protection, cells were aerosolised from solutions of hydroxyhexanes. However, all the straight chain hexanes with one, two or three hydroxyl groups in different positions on the hexane chain proved very toxic. This was taken to indicate that the protection by glucose must be afforded by the glucopyranose ring structure. To test this assumption cells were sprayed from a 10 per cent solution of α-methyl glucoside at 30 per cent RH and it was found that by the methylation of glucose all its protective action was lost. In the knowledge that the amino group might also be protective, cells were then aerosolised from 10 per cent solutions of glucosamine and N-acetyl glucosamine and while glucosamine was highly protective at 30 per cent RH N-acetylation only destroyed its protective action during the 0 to one hour period. (Webb, S. J. 1960a).

### The Effect of −NH$_2$ and −OH Groups Postioned on a Six Carbon Ring

The preceding results were taken to mean that the amino group could afford stability to the cells at high RH, or during the early stages of aerosolisation at low RH, and that at lower RH levels (30 per cent) the secondary alcohol group was required to protect them. Since a ring structure seemed to be necessary for protection, it was decided to examine the effects of both the -NH$_2$

and -OH groups substituted, in different positions, on a six carbon ring. Owing to solubility problems it was not always possible
to use the same weight/volume ratios of the compounds in water.
Where solubility allowed, 1 per cent solutions were used, the
less soluble compounds were used as saturated solutions.

In an initial study, the action of phenol and polyhydroxyben-
zenes were compared with those of polyhydroxycyclohexanes. All
the hydroxy-benzenes were extremely toxic, but the hydroxycyclohexanes were protective. Little difference could be found between
the *o*-, *p*- and *m*- dihydroxycyclohexanes, but the degree of protection seemed to increase with the number of $-OH$ groups
on the cyclohexane ring, with inositol affording the greatest degree of protection. In order to simplify the presentation of these
results, Table 2-IV was compiled. In this, the mean death rates
of cells over a five-hour period of air suspension at two levels of

TABLE 2-IV

THE MEAN DEATH RATES OF *S. marcescens* OVER A FIVE-HOUR PERIOD OF AIR SUS-
PENSION WHEN AEROSOLISED FROM VARIOUS SOLUTIONS

| Compound 1% Solution in $H_2O$ | Death Rates* ($K_5$) | |
|---|---|---|
| | 30% RH | 50% RH |
| Water | 0.046 | 0.029 |
| Aniline | 0.039 | 0.018 |
| Acetanilide | 0.051 | 0.028 |
| o-Phenylenediamine | 0.038 | 0.006 |
| m-Phenylenediamine | 0.037 | 0.007 |
| p-Phenylenediamine | 0.031 | 0.009 |
| o-Aminoacetanilide | 0.047 | 0.019 |
| m-Aminoacetanilide | 0.046 | 0.025 |
| p-Aminoacetanilide | 0.048 | 0.028 |
| Phenol | | |
| Catechol | | |
| Resorcinol | | |
| Hydroquinone | All cells dead after 1 hr. | |
| Pyrogallol | | |
| Phloroglucinol | | |
| Polyhydroxybenzene | | |
| 0-Dihydroxycyclohexane | 0.012 | 0.012 |
| m-Dihydroxycyclohexane | 0.010 | 0.013 |
| p-Dihydroxycyclohexane | 0.013 | 0.009 |
| 1-3-5 Trihydroxycyclohexane | 0.010 | 0.009 |
| 1-2-3 Trihydroxycyclohexane | 0.008 | 0.009 |
| Inositol | 0.006 | 0.007 |
| o-Aminophenol | 0.009 | 0.028 |
| m-Aminophenol | 0.044 | 0.018 |
| p-Aminophenol | 0.025 | 0.025 |
| 2-Aminorescorcinol | 0.002 | 0.026 |

*Each figure represents the average of three experiments.
Taken from Webb, S. J., *Canad. J. Microbiol. 6*, (1960a).

RH (30 per cent and 50 per cent) are presented. As described in Chapter 1, the decay constant for the combined 0 to one hour, and one to five-hour periods is designated $K_5$.

When concentration effects were studied, it was found that the concentration giving maximal protection varied with each compound, as did the degree of protection (Table 2-V). It was noticed that the concentrations of glucose was very similar to that reported by Gordon and Turner (1956) for the protection of guinea pig complement against heat inactivation at $53 °C$. These authors also reported that dulcitol had no protective action.

TABLE 2-V

THE DEATH RATES OF *S. marcescens* AEROSOLISED FROM SOLUTIONS OF VARIOUS STABILISING COMPOUNDS AT $25 °C$.

| Compound | Optimal Concentration | Mean Death Rate Over 5 Hour Period | |
|---|---|---|---|
| | | 30% RH | 50% RH |
| Water | — | 0.046 | 0.029 |
| Bacto-Protone | 12.5% | — | 0.005 |
| Glucose | 20.0% | 0.017 | 0.014 |
| Glucosamine | 20.0% | 0.007 | 0.007 |
| o-Phenylenediamine | 1.0% | 0.038 | 0.006 |
| o-Aminophenol | 1.0% | 0.009 | 0.028 |
| Inositol | 6.0% | 0.006 | 0.004 |

Taken from Webb, S. J., *Canad. J. Microbiol.* 6, (1960a).

The significant feature from these data was the gross toxicity of the hydroxybenzenes and the protectiveness of the hydroxy-cyclohexanes which indicated that the substituted hydrogen atoms were involved in the protective mechanism. It seemed reasonable to assume then that the −OH group was the effective group, an assumption supported by the anomaly of o-aminophenol and 2-aminoresorcinol. These compounds seemed to protect the cells at 30 per cent RH whereas at 50 per cent RH they had no protective ability. The experimental data suggested, therefore, that both the −OH, and the −NH$_2$ groups on a six carbon ring could protect the cells at some stage against aerosol death, the -NH$_2$ group being effective at 50 per cent RH and above, or during the early stages only at lower RH levels but at 30 per cent RH and the −OH group was the effective group.

The fact that only the o-aminophenol effectively stabilised the cells indicated that one hydrogen of the amino group was behaving in a similar manner to the hydrogen in the hydroxycyclo-hexane structure. This was supported by the protectiveness of 2-aminoresorcinol at 30 per cent RH. It seemed, therefore, that an ortho substituted amino group could prevent the toxic action of the primary phenolic hydroxyl group and the complete lack of protection by *m*-amino phenol made it appear that steric factors and bond distances were important in the protective mechanism.

There was too, the possibility that the nature of the ring structure of the compounds might also be an important factor in determining their activity. For example, the resonance of the hydroxybenzenes, as opposed to the non-resonance of inosital might in some way account for the differences in their action.

## The Influence of the Ring Nuclei of Cyclic Compounds

In order to determine whether or not the nucleus of the compound had any effect, cells were aerosolised from water and solutions of resorcinol, 2:4-dihydroxypyridine, 2:6-dihydroxy, 1:4 diazine and uracil, and there was a marked difference in the behaviour of these three compounds (Table 2-VI). Unfortunately, the hexahydroxy derivatives of the compounds were not available. It appeared that the introduction of a nitrogen atom into the ring led to reduced toxicity as compared with resorcinol, while two nitrogen atoms in the ring produced a compound that was notably protective during the one to five-hour period of aerosolisation and slightly protective in the other periods in comparison with water.

All the varied effects of the added compounds on air-borne

TABLE 2-VI

THE EFFECT OF THE RING NUCLEUS OF DIHYDROXY COMPOUNDS ON THE DEATH RATES OF *S. marcescens* AND *E. coli* AT 30% RH AND 25°C.

| | Death Rates | | | |
|---|---|---|---|---|
| Compound | $K_1$ (0-1 hr) | | $K_2$ (1-5 hr) | |
| | A | B | A | B |
| Water | 0.046 | 0.044 | 0.046 | 0.041 |
| Resorcinol | No recovery | | No recovery | |
| 2:4 Dihydroxy Pyridine | 0.041 | 0.044 | 0.031 | 0.033 |
| 2:6 Dihydroxy-1:4 diazine | 0.034 | 0.030 | 0.009 | 0.010 |
| Uracil | 0.032 | 0.030 | 0.005 | 0.005 |

Taken from Webb, S. J.: *Can. J. Microbiol.* 6, (1960a).
A = *S. marcescens*
B = *E. coli*

cells were similar for *S. marcescens, E. coli* and *B. subtilis,* but
with *Staph. albus* there was only a little protection by inositol at
a very low **RH** (30 per cent) during the first hour. However,
because of the inherently high aerosol stability of this organism,
the difference between the death rates of water and inositol aerosolised *Staph. albus* cells would, in any case, only be very small.
With the exception of NaCl, toxic compounds such as phenol,
resorcinol and glycol were as toxic to the staphylococcus as they
were to the other organisms.

**The Effect of Added Chemicals on the Water Content of Cells**

It was observed that all of the protective compounds not only
contained six membered rings but also contained groups that
might be able to replace water molecules (H-O-H) in the cell
during desiccation and all contained groups able to combine with
proteins by hydrogen bonding. Fry and Grieves (1951) found
that glucose increased the survival of freeze dried bacteria and
suggested that this might be due to the retention of water by
the glucose: since methylation destroyed the protective action of
glucose on air-borne cells, the retention of water hypothesis did
not in this instance seem to explain the action of glucose. It was
considered more likely that, since both structural and steric
factors appeared to be involved, some combination between the
cellular constituents and the protective compounds occurred
whereby a collapse of the structure of the latter on desiccation was
prevented. The combination between cellular molecules and
compound would have to be by means of bonds similar in
strength to protein-water bonds and be reversible with water.
It would be possible, therefore, for compounds such as glycerols
and glycol to do two things while the cells were drying:

1. Compete with molecular groups for available water
   molecules, and
2. Combine irreversibly with the cell macromolecules and
   destroy their native structures.

Similarly, any compound not having a six membered ring nucleus
and possessing groups with strong water affinities would be expected to be toxic to the air-borne cells. Thus, it seemed possible

that the ketonic group of sorbose by virtue of its strong water affinity or H-bonding strength might override the protectiveness of its secondary alcohol groups. Similarly, the presence of a primary alcohol group and an oxygen atom in glucosepyranose could account for the small protection by the secondary alcohol groups of glucose as opposed to those of inositol.

It seemed pertinent, therefore, at this stage, to study the relationship between cellular water and cell death and the effect of the added substances on these relationships.

The refractive index of cells suspended in water and solutions was obtained using an AO Baker interference microscope. Measurements were made with a 1 mm. (x100) shearing objective in green light provided by a Baker 390B mercury arc lamp. The maximum retardation in phase of light passing through the cells was measured by extinction point measurements, first in preparations mounted in distilled water and then in solutions of various compounds. The refractive index was then calculated from equation 2-1 and solid content from equation 2-2.

*Equation 2-1*

$$n_s = n_m + \theta\lambda/360t$$

where  $n_s$ = refractive index of cells in the medium
       $n_m$ = refractive index of medium
       $\theta$  = mean retardation in phase of light
       $t$  = thickness of cell ($0.7\mu$)

*Equation 2-2*

$$\lambda = \text{wavelength of light}$$
$$C = \frac{n_s - n_m}{\alpha}$$

where  $C$ = percentage of solids
       $\alpha$ = refractive increment of cellular solids
              (0.0018, see Barer and Joseph, 1954; Hale, 1958)

The refractive index of the cells was also determined by light scattering measurements using a Coleman Nepho-Colorimeter No. 9 modified to collect all light scattered through 120° from the incident beam. In the calculations, it was necessary to utilise the refractive index of cells suspended in water, found with the interference microscope, and the refractive indices of the suspending fluids, obtained from the International Critical Tables. With these quantities known, it was possible to calculate the refractive index of the cells from equation 2-3 (Kruyt, 1952).

*Equation 2-3*

$$\frac{I_1}{I_2} = \frac{n^2 - n_m^2}{n_w^2 + 2n_m^2} \times \frac{n_s^2 + 2n_m^2}{n_s^2 - n_m^2}$$

where $I_1$ = total light scattered by cells in water
$\quad\;\; I_2$ = total light scattered by cells in solution
$\quad\;\; n_m$ = refractive index of suspending medium
$\quad\;\; n_w$ = refractive index of cells in water
$\quad\;\; n_s$ = refractive index of cells in solution
$I_1$ and $I_2$ were measured in Coleman Nephelos units.

Mager *et al.*, in 1956, observed that cells suspended in salt solution scattered more light than cells suspended in water. Since Edsall *et al.* (1950) and Friend *et al.* (1951) were able to detect the binding of $Ca^{++}$ and dodecyl sulphate respectively to serum albumin by light scattering measurements, it seemed possible that the increased scatter by bacterial cells was due to combination between the cellular macro-molecules and the added substance. Light scattering measurements were made, therefore, on a constant number of cells suspended in different solutions.

In order to make calculations of water content from these measurements, it was necessary to know the refractive index of cells suspended in water, and since similar measurements had been made by Ross and Billing (1957) using an interference microscope, it was decided to use that technique. Small changes have been observed in the refractive index of serum solutions when sulphanilamide is added (Klotz, 1953), and in gelatine solutions on the addition of detergent (Pankhurst and Smith, 1947) both authors attributing this to protein compound complexes. It seemed reasonable, therefore, to use the interference microscope to check the refractive indices calculated from light scatter measurements.

Tables 2-VII and 2-VIII give respectively, the light scatter, in Nephelos units of suspensions containing $1\times10^8$ cells/ml. in various solutions, and the mean phase retardations of light by films of the same organism, together with the calculated mean refractive indices. As can be seen, there was remarkably good agreement between the results by the two techniques, and a statistical analysis of the results suggested that each of the first four indices were significantly different from one another.

TABLE 2-VII

THE LIGHT SCATTER IN NEPHELOS UNITS BY $1 \times 10^8$ CELLS/ML. IN VARIOUS SOLUTIONS (S. marcescens)

| Suspending Fluid | Light Scatter* | | | | | Mean | Mean Refractive Index |
|---|---|---|---|---|---|---|---|
| $H_2O$ | 24.5 | 24.6 | 24.5 | 24.5 | 24.7 | 24.5 | — |
| 5% Glucose | 36.4 | 36.2 | 36.3 | 36.2 | 36.1 | 36.3 | 1.401 |
| 5% Glucosamine | 33.6 | 33.3 | 33.8 | 33.6 | 33.3 | 33.5 | 1.398 |
| 5% Inositol | 30.3 | 30.5 | 30.3 | 30.4 | 30.4 | 30.4 | 1.396 |
| 5% NaCl | 45.8 | 45.9 | 46.0 | 45.9 | 45.8 | 45.9 | 1.406 |
| 5% Glucose+ 5% NaCl | 36.5 | 36.3 | 36.4 | 36.1 | 36.3 | 36.3 | 1.401 |
| 5% Inositol+ 5% NaCl | 34.1 | 33.8 | 34.0 | 33.5 | 33.3 | 33.7 | 1.399 |

*The five figures are from five separate suspensions, each figure represents the average of six readings taken at intervals of one minute.
Taken from Webb, S. J., Canad. J. Microbiol. 6, (1960b).

TABLE 2-VIII

THE REFRACTIVE INDEX OF S. marcescens SUSPENDED IN VARIOUS SOLUTIONS. CALCULATED FROM INTERFERENCE MICROSCOPE MEASUREMENTS

| Suspending Fluid | Angular Phase Retardation* | | | | | | Mean | Index |
|---|---|---|---|---|---|---|---|---|
| Water | 22.4 | 22.6 | 22.3 | 22.4 | 22.5 | 22.3 | 22.4 | 1.382 |
| 5% Glucose | 27.5 | 27.7 | 27.6 | 27.6 | 27.8 | 27.5 | 27.6 | 1.400 |
| 5% Glucosamine | 26.6 | 26.5 | 26.4 | 26.5 | 26.3 | 26.5 | 26.4 | 1.397 |
| 5% Inositol | 25.3 | 25.3 | 25.5 | 25.2 | 25.3 | 25.2 | 25.3 | 1.395 |
| 5% NaCl | 33.0 | 33.4 | 33.2 | 33.1 | 33.2 | 33.2 | 33.2 | 1.405 |
| 5% Glucose+ 5% NaCl | 27.4 | 27.7 | 27.7 | 27.4 | 27.8 | 27.2 | 27.5 | 1.400 |
| 5% Inositol+ 5% NaCl | 26.7 | 26.8 | 27.0 | 26.9 | 26.5 | 27.1 | 26.8 | 1.398 |

*Each of the six figures represents the average of three readings taken from different areas of the slide. Six slides were prepared from separate suspensions, five of which had been used previously for light scatter measurements.
Taken from Webb, S. J., Canad. J. Microbiol. 6, (1960b).

The close agreement between the two techniques suggested that the increase in light scatter and refractive index were due to a combination between protein and the added compounds. It was noted that NaCl produced the largest change and inositol the smallest, and since it has been reported that the Cl⁻ ion can displace bonded water from wool (McPhee, 1959) it seemed possible that a similar phenomenon was occurring within the cell. Assuming the specific volume of cellular solids to be 0.75 (Barer and Joseph, 1954) water contents were calculated from the refractive indices and compared with those calculated from dry weight measurements. The results are presented in Table 2-IX and it is evident that while the light scatter and interferometry techniques gave very similar results, the values determined from dry weights were, in every case, higher by approximately 10 per cent. This was assumed to be due to water trapped between the cells after sedimentation, which would not be measured by the other techniques, because it agrees well with the amount calculated to be trapped in pellets of cells by the radioactive techniques of Cowie and Roberts (1955). All three methods, therefore, showed extremely good agreement. In all cases, the cell seemed to contain slightly smaller amounts of water than those suspended in water, the differences ranging from 1 to 2 per cent for inositol to 10 per cent for NaCl. This was noteworthy as inositol, which produced the smallest change was the most effective stabiliser of air-borne cells, whereas NaCl, which produced large changes, was toxic.

TABLE 2-IX
THE PERCENTAGE OF WATER IN CELLS OF *S. marcescens* CALCULATED FROM REFRACTIVE INDEX AND DRY WEIGHT MEASUREMENTS

| Suspending Fluid | Dry Weight* | Refractive Index Light Scatter | Refractive Index Interferometry |
|---|---|---|---|
| Water | 88.1 | — | 79.2 |
| 5% Glucose | 84.5 | 74.6 | 75.0 |
| 5% Glucosamine | 85.6 | 75.8 | 76.4 |
| 5% Inositol | 87.2 | 76.7 | 77.1 |
| 5% NaCl | 80.4 | 70.0 | 70.4 |
| 5% Glucose+ 5% NaCl | 83.4 | 74.6 | 75.1 |
| 5% Inositol+ 5% NaCl | 85.2 | 75.4 | 75.8 |

*Each figure represents the average of six separate determinations on cells from the same culture as was used for light scatter and interferometry.

Some of this water was undoubtedly displaced because of the increased mass of the cellular fluid, but since this amount would be very small, it was assumed that some of the water was actively displaced by a combination of the substance and protein. This could only occur if the ions or molecules were competing for adsorption sites on macromolecules. Further, no change in refractive index should have been detected, by either of the above methods, if combination or density changes in the cellular solids had not occurred. The fact that the light scatter refractive indices were so close to those calculated from interferometry suggested also that change in cell size was either not responsible for the increased light scatter or was of little importance. Significantly, the refractive index change produced by NaCl alone was reduced, in the presence of either inositol or glucose, to approximately that produced by the latter compounds, and the water content by dry weight measurement was also higher. This seemed to indicate that these two compounds were able to prevent the Cl⁻ion from displacing water.

The above experiments also demonstrated that the added compounds were quickly taken up by the cell and that equilibrium with the external fluid was established. If this had not been so. the water contents calculated from refractive indices would have been far greater than those from dry weight measurements. Also, Cowie and Roberts (1955) demonstrated that some gram-negative cells are freely permeable to ions, small molecules, sugars and peptides. It is of interest to note here that the extremely air stable Gram-positive organisms, *Staph. albus* and *Staph. citreus* did not show this increase in refractive index when suspended in different fluids while Mitchell (1953) has demonstrated that staphylococci are impermeable by passive diffusion to some ions and molecules and that active transport is necessary to carry molecules into the cell. Dry weight measurements and refractive index measurements indicated that staphylococci contain less water than the gram-negative *S. marcescens* and *E. coli,* their water content being approximately that of *S. marcescens* suspended in inositol (Table 2-X). Therefore, it was assumed that, by adding inositol, a macromolecule-inositol complex was formed and that this complex was in equilibrium with macromolecular-water complexes whilst in a liquid environment. As desiccation occurred, however, the equilibrium would move toward the inositol complex. This type of system would be similar to that described by Cann (1959), who stated that the difference in the electrophoretic patterns of proteins in buffers containing carboxylic acids was probably due to complexes of proteins with undissociated molecules and that these complexes were in equilibrium with the normal protein.

TABLE 2-X

THE WATER CONTENT OF SEVERAL ORGANISMS AS INDICATED FROM REFRACTIVE INDEX MEASUREMNTS

| Organism | Refractive Index | Water Content (%) |
|----------|------------------|-------------------|
| S. marcescens | 1.382 | 79.2 |
| E. coli | 1.383 | 79.0 |
| Staph. albus | 1.394 | 74.6 |
| Staph. citreus | 1.396 | 73.7 |
| B. subtilis | 1.390 | 76.3 |
| N. catarrhalis | 1.388 | 77.5 |

Taken from Webb, S. J., *Canad. J. Microbiol. 6*, (1960b).

In the case of inositol and the protective amino compounds, it was difficult to visualise any combination other than through hydrogen bonding. Forbes and Knight (1959) were able to show that the intramolecular hydrogen bonds between benzoic acid molecules were continually formed, broken and reformed and that "the characteristic ultraviolet spectrum of this compound was only evident if the bonds were formed often enough." It seemed reasonable then that a dynamic system between macro-molecular-water and macromolecular-compound could exist in equilibrium provided the bonds between the protein-water and the protein-compound were of equal strength.

**The Effect of Changes in Molecular Structure of Cell Components and the Possible Role of Hydrogen Bonds**

In aerosols, the cells are in a gaseous environment and water exchanges only involve the "bound water" and water vapour in the air. The secondary alcohol groups of inositol, hydroxycyclo-hexanes and the amino groups of aniline etc., were presumed able, therefore, to replace $H_2O$ molecules and maintain structure through hydrogen bonding.

To test these assumptions it was considered that:

1. Known protein hydrogen bond breaking substances such as urea should interfere with the protective action of inositol:

2. NaCl, by being able to displace bonded water, should also be able to displace inositol:

3. A strain with an altered protein structure should show different aerosol characteristics, and

4. If the configuration of the added substance was important, compounds with the same empirical formula, but not structure, should affect the air-borne cells differently.

Cells were aerosolised, therefore, in solutions of 6 per cent inositol with and without 1M urea, guanidine and thiourea and various concentrations of NaCl. To test the need for correct configuration of the added compound, cells were aerosolised from solutions of 5 per cent glycine, which had previously been found to be slightly protective, and 5 per cent glycolomide. Since it has been abundantly shown that chloramphenicol inhibits protein synthesis, it follows that a drug resistant strain should possess different structures from the sensitive strain. A resistant strain of *S. marcescens* was developed on chloramphenicol gradient plates and aerosolised from distilled water. Also, the sensitive strain was aerosolised from solutions of chloramphenicol and other antibiotics.

The results of these experiments are presented in Tables 2-XI and 2-XII. It can be seen that urea and guanidine were toxic and seriously inhibited the action of inositol. Thiourea, on the other hand, was protective, but did not interfere with the protection of inositol. Also, a marked difference between the action of glycine and glycolamide was observed, the latter being so toxic that all the cells were dead in one hour. This resembled the action of

urea and was taken to indicate that the $-C\underset{\diagdown O}{\overset{\diagup NH_2}{}}$ group was responsible.

| Glycolamide | Glycine | Urea |
|:---:|:---:|:---:|
| H | H | |
| $\mid$ | $\mid$ | $\diagup NH_2$ |
| $HO - C - C \underset{\diagdown O}{\overset{\diagup NH_2}{}}$ | $NH_2 - C - COOH$ | $C = O$ |
| $\mid$ | $\mid$ | $\diagdown NH_2$ |
| H | H | |

TABLE 2-XI

THE EFFECT OF VARIOUS COMPOUNDS ON THE ACTION OF INOSITOLS IN AEROSOLS OF S. *marcescens* AT 30% RH

| | Mean Death Rate 5 Hours ($K_5$) | |
|---|---|---|
| Suspending Fluid | Compound Alone | Compound Plus 6% Inositol |
| 6% Inositol | 0.006 | — |
| 5% Urea | No recovery | 0.019 |
| 5% Guanidine | 0.038 | 0.023 |
| 5% Thiourea | 0.024 | 0.008 |
| 0.1% NaCl | 0.105 (one hour $K_1$) | 0.005 |
| 0.5% NaCl | 0.104 (one hour $K_1$) | 0.018 |
| 1.0% NaCl | 0.108 (one hour $K_1$) | 0.020 |
| 5.0% NaCl | 0.116 (one hour $K_1$) | 0.038 |
| 5.0% Glycine | 0.016 | 0.001 |
| 5.0% Glycolamide | No recovery | 0.037 |
| $H_2O$ | 0.046 | 0.006 |

Taken from Webb, S. J., *Canad. J. Microbiology* 6, (1960a).

TABLE 2-XII

THE EFFECT OF THE BOUND WATER CONTENT OF SEMI-DRIED CELLS OF S. *marcescens* ON THE ACTION OF CHEMICAL ADDITIVES

| | | Approximate Water Content of cells/100 gms cell Solid | | |
|---|---|---|---|---|
| | | 4 | 15 | 30 |
| Inositol | (5%) | 0.006* | 0.006 | 0.005 |
| Thiourea | (5%) | 0.027 | 0.032 | 0.056 |
| Sodium Arsenite | (1.0%) | 0.012 | 0.048 | 0.114 |
| 2-Aminoresorcinol | (0.5%) | 0.004 | 0.034 | 0.138 |
| $H_2O$ | | 0.046 | 0.036 | 0.004 |

*Death rate during the 0 to 1 hr. ($K_1$) period.

Further, glycolamide inhibited the action of inositol whereas glycine did not, and it seemed reasonable to assume that compounds with this group were able to hydrogen bond to peptide or similar groupings, and possibly change the structure of macromolecules irreversibly.

The chloramphenicol resistant strain was found to be more resistant to aerosol death than the sensitive strain Webb (1959). Surprisingly, however, the same stability was afforded cells by suspending them in a 0.25 per cent solution of the drug prior to aerosolisation. Also, of several antibiotics tested only chloramphenicol and some tetracyclines stabilised the cells, although it was later found that the concentration of the antibiotics was important. Concentrated solutions of terramycin, aureomycin, and albamycin were toxic.

It appeared, therefore, that the change in molecular structures produced by antibiotic resistance gave the cells a greater aerosol stability. The fact that suspension in the antibiotics prior to aerosolisation also produced stability was taken to indicate that the drugs behaved in a similar manner to inositol, and were bonding with the cellular macromolecules.

## Electron Microscopy

In an endeavor to observe these changes by electron microscopy, air-borne cells were deposited on newly made collodion membranes and examined. In such an examination, the cells are subjected to heat and low vacuum and it must be presumed that they are completely dehydrated. At any rate, no difference could be seen in the appearance of cells from an aerosol and those placed on the membrane from a suspension in water or solution. A second difficulty was that when cells suspended in solutions were used the solute crystallised out on the membrane, and either obscured the cells or caused the membrane to break, and it was found necessary to wash the prepared specimen with water before examination. In only one case was a fairly clear region found on a membrane on which cells had been deposited from an aerosol of inositol suspended bacteria.

It was apparent that severe shrinkage of the electron dense material occurs in the absence of small amounts of solutes and when inositol was present the shrinkage was more regular. These observations suggested that even with complete dehydration inositol could prevent severe distortion of the protein structure. However, the fact that small amounts of solutes seemed to be able to prevent shrinkage indicated that shrinkage itself was not necessarily responsible for death. Also, it was later found that both NaCl and glucose prevented obvious shrinkage, yet NaCl was extremely toxic to air-borne cells.

Since, in the aerosol, the cells would not be subjected to high temperatures or low vacuum, it was reasoned that the changes in molecular structure due to water loss were of a very subtle nature and that the toxicity of certain compounds such as urea and NaCl were also due to similar small changes.

The results so far had indicated that the removal of bonded water from the cellular protein was responsible for death but there still remained the possibility of atmospheric oxydations. However, when cells were aerosolised from water into atmospheres of nitrogen, carbondioxide and air enriched with oxygen, very little difference in death rates was detected.

**The Relationship Between the Structure of Added Chemicals, Water and the Death of Air-dried Cells**

At this stage of our investigations, it was quite clear that changes in the structure of a macromolecule within the cell occurred on desiccation and also that compounds with strategically placed -OH, -NH₂ and possibly -SH groups could prevent this change. Therefore, we turned our attention to the inter-relationship between RH and 2-aminoresorcinol, thiourea, inositol, several pyrimidines and sodium arsenite, the latter having been found to offer some protection to cells at low relative humidities. The results, tabulated in Table 2-XII, demonstrate some interesting findings. All of the compounds, with the exception of inositol and the pyrimidines, were highly toxic at RH levels above 60 per cent and interfered with the protective action of inositol. On the other hand, all were protective at 30 per cent RH, so that the survival vs RH pattern found with water aerosolised cells was completely reversed. This latter phenomenon was observed, also, with Rous sarcoma virus aerosolised in citrate buffer (Webb, Bather and Hodges, 1963). Knowing how the water content of the cells varied with RH, it could only be assumed that not only was the removal of water lethal, but the re-orientation of water under the influence of hydrated chemicals was equally, if not more lethal.

Thus, it appeared that the toxicity or protectiveness of a compound relied on the amount of water present in the cell and that the latter controlled the type of bonding made between the chemical and cell macromolecules. The correct positioning of water in these macromolecules, therefore, seemed all important. Pre-

sumably when water is absent, or almost absent, compounds such
as 2-aminoresorcinal are able to place themselves in positions
which are protective to macromolecules. The above assumptions
were rendered more plausible by the demonstrated interference
by such compounds with the action of inositol and the complete
absence of toxicity by inositol itself. The $\diagdown_{OH}^{\diagup H}$ groups of
inositol are almost identical, physico-chemically, to water, so
presumably the binding of water to inositol would result in a
structure similar to that of water-water blocks and hence no toxicity should result, and in fact, it did not. The toxicity of salts
(Table 2-XI), and of other compounds at high RH levels was
also reduced by inositol, whereas, its protective action was lowered. This strongly suggested that binding between inositol and
these compounds occurred and so water-compound binding
seemed a reasonable explanation of the described findings (Table
2-XII). The action of the tested pyrimidines indicated that the
position of the protective groups on the ring nucleus was important and different positions were required for maximal protection as the water content was changed (Webb, 1963). Such
findings add to those mentioned above with other types of compounds. Thus, the kind of interaction between the bound water
of macromolecules, or the groups of the macromolecule itself
with an added chemical seemed to determine the fate of an air-
borne cell.

Finally, it was necessary to check that the protection or toxicity
of the added compounds was due to an action in the aerosol. We
already knew 1.0 per cent NaCl to be toxic to the airborne cells
and had no toxic action in the impinger. However, instead of
saline, solutions of sucrose of up to 20 per cent, inositol, glycerol
and various other compounds were used to collect cells aerosolised
from water and held at 30 per cent RH. In no case was the recovery significantly changed over that found when saline was used.
Therefore, the addition of a protective or toxic compound to the
cells after aerosolization did not appear to change the normal
behaviour of 30 per cent RH water atomized cells. It seemed
reasonably clear then that the various actions of the added chem-

icals on the cells were taking place in the aerosol and were a direct
result of partial desiccation.

## Conclusion and Discussion

A large amount of work has been conducted on the use of
glycols as aerial disinfectants (Wells and Zapposodi, 1948; Robertson *et al.* 1943; Lester *et al.* 1949; Wells, 1955), so it was no surprise that glycols proved toxic to air-borne cells. However, the
workers cited above have reported that the toxicity of glycols to
air-borne cells was a function of RH, some being more toxic at
high RH and others at low RH. It was also noted that even at
high concentrations glycols were not toxic to cells suspended in
glycol solutions. The toxicity, therefore, was associated with desiccation of the cells. Glycerol behaved likewise and was protective at
some RH levels especially to cells dried slowly on filters.

In the present studies, all the polyhydroxy straight chain compounds tested were toxic to the air-borne cells and it was not until
compounds such as glucose, glucosamine and hydroxycyclohexanes, with a six-membered ring were used that large degrees of
protection became apparent. This strongly indicates that configuration and steric factors are important in determining whether the
action of the compound is toxic or protective to the cells. It is
felt that the need for a ring structure is due to the necessity for
the compound to have the correct size and shape to fit into or
between macromolecules, for it is highly possible that protein
molecules have a hexagonal shape. (Bernal and Fankuchen, 1941).

The behaviour of the compounds was strongly dependent on
RH and it is evident that the peaks in death rates at 60 to 65 per
cent RH observed by other workers (Dunklin and Puck, 1948),
are due to the action of solutes, in particular NaCl. Where cells
are aerosolised from a growth medium it is apparent that even
if the medium is well defined, but contains a protein hydrolysate,
the degree of hydrolysis of the original medium constituent, or
the degree to which it has hydrolysed due to microbial metabolism, will affect the subsequent death rate of the cells in air. It is
possible also that some of the apparent loss of aerial stability of
cells after liquid storage in their growth medium is due to slow

hydrolysis of the nitrogenous compounds of the medium. The products of metabolism will also affect the characteristics of the death of cells aerosolized from a growth medium. If glycerol or glycol was produced, peaks in death rate could appear at 30 per cent, 60 per cent or 80 per cent RH, depending on the compound: and if peptones were formed in the presence of NaCl a peak could occur at 60 per cent RH, and so on. The apparent discrepancies between workers concerning RH effects are undoubtedly due to the failure to recognise the large effects of the medium from which the cells are aerosolized. The effect of solutes on air-borne cells makes it appear that they interfere with the relationship between cellular water and atmospheric water vapour. It is thus assumed that compounds with groups having a stronger affinity for water than the groups of macromolecules will compete for their water and bring about a change in their structure. Low (1953) discovered that proteins definitely shrink when alcohols replace their water. Also, should there be insufficient water, the solute may combine with the protein itself and by making strong hydrogen bond bridges bring about irreversible structural change.

The importance of structural and steric configuration is due, in all probability, to the need for the solute not only to fit into the macromolecules, but to combine with it in such a manner as to preserve its natural configuration. That structure is involved is clearly demonstrated by the action of the various chemicals tested. Since the methylation of one of the secondary alcohol groups of glucose destroyed its protective ability, it can be argued that it is this group that is protective. However, a more likely explanation is that the carbonyl and primary alcohol groups, having a strong water affinity, are toxic and counteract the protective action of the secondary alcohol groups. This explanation is strengthened by the tremendous protective ability of inositol. The author was unable to detect any difference in the rate of evaporation of water from films of cells filtered out from water, glucose or inositol solutions. The rate of water loss seemed to follow first order kinetics, agreeing with McMeeken and Warner (1942), and the activation energies were the same. However, there appeared to be a difference in the quantity of water that could be removed but this water was not being held by the solutes but actively displaced.

The fact that amino and the secondary alcohol groups afforded cellular aerosol protection is a strong indication that these groups replace water molecules and that since they would not be subject to any equilibrium exchanges, they are able to maintain structure and hence the viability of air-borne cells for a long time. Further, very strong evidence to support this is the increase in protective ability with increased number of hydroxyl groups on the cyclohexane nucleus. There is, nevertheless, the problem of the gross toxicity of the hydroxybenzenes. This is assumed to be due to the lack of a second hydrogen atom with each of the OH groups, an hypothesis supported by the protectiveness of o-aminophenol and 2-aminoresorcinol and the lack of protectiveness of meta aminophenol. It is possible that one of the amino hydrogen atoms of aminophenols can function in the same way as the H atoms of the hydroxycyclohexanes, provided that the amino group is ortho to the hydroxyl. This explanation appeared reasonable until it was found that uracil also afforded some protection and it now seems that two nitrogen atoms in the ring nucleus can prevent also the toxicity of the OH groups; but protection is only apparent during the later stages of aerosolization. It is noticeable that the toxicity of the OH group gradually decreased as the number of N atoms in the ring nucleus increased, and since it is known that the OH group becomes less acid when placed on a pyrimidine ring it must be assumed that protection is due to this phenomenon. Ortho substitution of an amino group in phenols will also reduce the acidity of the -OH group and hence its H bonding power, however, from the standpoint of cell stabilization the change in -OH activity due to an -NH$_2$ group may not always be advantageous. Experiments on the action of uracil and aminouracils indicated that a protective -OH group may be rendered inactive (Webb, 1963). Possibly the most significant point found from interaction between these two groups is that in no case was an -OH group rendered toxic by an adjacent -NH$_2$ group.

The similarity between all protective compounds, in that they all contain groups potentially capable of replacing water molecules and all possess groups able to form hydrogen bonds, strongly indicates that death and protection therefrom are due to the breaking and making respectively of hydrogen bonds. The actual reason for inactivity may well be the formation of very strong inter or intra molecular H-bonds or even covalent links irreversible with water after the removal of water, and it has been suggested that this process can occur in some protein crystals (Waugh, 1954).

The involvement of hydrogen bonding is made more evident by the action of urea and guanidine on air-borne cells. These two substances from very strong hydrogen bonds and are extremely toxic to air stored cells. Urea denaturation of proteins in solution is reversible (Harris, 1956), but after dehydration it appears to become irreversible. It is also known that chloride and sulphate ions will retard urea denaturation of arachin (Johnson and Naismith, 1956; Naismith and Williams, 1959) and it was found in the present study that these ions will inhibit the toxicity of urea toward air-borne cells. The salts alone, however, were extremely toxic.

The results of these experiments gave strong support to the working hypothesis described in chapter one, and also led to the discovery of inositol as an excellent protective agent not only for bacteria, but also for viruses. With this compound we were now able to turn our attention to the physiological changes induced in cells by desiccation using inositol protected cells as controls.

# CHAPTER 3

# THE PHYSIOLOGICAL EFFECTS OF BOUND WATER LOSS

## The Activity of Constitutive Enzymes

A T THIS POINT OF OUR INVESTIGATIONS, it seemed clear that the removal of water bound to cell macromolecules resulted in death, but the precise reason was unknown. Several possibilities existed, from damage to the cell membrane to the inactivation of a vital macromolecule, and our first task was to examine the effect of drying on several enzyme systems of the cell.

In order to determine the metabolic functions of the cell protected by inositol, non-dried and cells dried in inositol acted as controls. However, as it proved impossible to collect a sufficient number of cells from the aerosol for physiological studies, film drying had to be used. This was done by placing 1.0 ml. of washed cells resuspended in water or inositol on a millipore filter and transferring the film to a drying cabinet pre-set to a given level of RH and temperature. The non-dried controls were treated likewise except drying was not allowed to take place. The death rate of cells on these filters was considerably slower than in aerosols and depended on the number of cells per filter. In our first experiments too many cells were used and considerable protection of water dried cells was noted, presumably caused by a "skin" of dead cells interfering with subsequent drying. Strangely enough under these conditions inositol was toxic to the cells as were most other chemicals tested. The non-specificity of this type of killing suggested that prolonged drying created solutions of high osmotic pressure within the cell. To simulate the aerosol behaviour of cells about $1 \times 10^8$ cells per cm.$^2$ of filter were found satisfactory when viability counts were made at five minute intervals, however, approximately ten minutes drying was always required before any deaths were apparent. The procedure finally settled upon was to allow a ten minute equilibration period first, followed by up to an hour of drying, and under these conditions, assuming the non-dried cells to be 100 per cent viable, the cell counts at 30 per cent RH were as follows:

Water-dried
    24.4 to 33.6% (5 minutes)   1.9 to 2.7% (60 minutes)
Inositol-dried
    89.2 to 91.3% (5 minutes)   88.4 to 91% (60 minutes)

Initially, the ability of *E. coli* to oxidase glucose and several aminoacids was examined after prolonged drying periods of up to five hours, and the results published in 1961 (Webb).

In Table 3-I, the $O_2$ uptake $\mu l / hr$. of control and treated cells are tabulated. If these results were viewed in terms of wet weight of cells then it appeared that the rate of oxidation of the aminoacids was greatly reduced by desiccation and still further reduced by protection with inositol. Also, the rate of oxidation of glucose by the unprotected dried cells was reduced whereas that of the inositol protected cells was not. If, however, the results were analysed on the basis of viable cell numbers, then the situation became more complicated. For instance, the oxidation rates by all the unprotected cells would have to be multiplied by approximately fifty, (assuming an average viability of 2.0 per cent after drying), and under these circumstances the oxidation rate of

TABLE 3-I

THE EFFECT OF DRYING FOR 60 MINUTES AT 30% RELATIVE HUMIDITY ON THE ABILITY OF *E. coli* TO OXIDIZE GLUCOSE AND AMINO ACIDS AND TO DECARBOXYLATE L-ARGININE

| Compound | Control | $H_2O$-dried | Inositol Dried |
|---|---|---|---|
| L-alanine* | 18. | 6 (2%) | 4 (90%) |
| L-serine* | 40. | 12 | 6 |
| Glutamic* | 16. | 3 | 8 |
| Glucose* | 72. | 45 | 78 |
| L-arginine↑ | 11. | 102 | 105 |

* $\mu l / O_2 / hr$.                    ( ) Approximate viability of cells
↑ $\mu l / CO_2 / hr$.                    No. of control cells $= 1 \times 10^9$ cells per flask.

glucose would reach a phenominal figure of somewhere about 2500 $\mu$l/hour.

Clearly, one could not correlate the reduction in rate of amino-acid oxidation with cell death because the protected cells displayed an equal reduction, but it was possible that the results reflected the relative ability of the aminoacid substrates to reach the enzyme systems of the cell. Perhaps inositol, through some combination with the membrane, had prevented the entry of aminoacids. However, when aminoacid decarboxylation was studied the very reverse was found. An increase in L-Arginine decarboxylase activity from 11$\mu$l/$CO_2$/hr. for non-dried cells to 105$\mu$l/hr. occurred on drying whether or not inositol was present, in fact, the increase was greatest in inositol dried cells (Table 3-1). This phenomenon also could not be correlated with viability or death as, apparently, high decarboxylase activity went on after the death of the cell and also in inositol protected live cells.

Unless one postulated different mechanisms governing the permeability of individual aminoacids, membrane damage as a cause of death did not seem realistic. Oxidation rates of aminoacids were reduced on drying while decarboxylation rates increased. One could argue, of course, that a severe change in anabolic to catabolic metabolism took place after drying, and this would have been reasonable were it not for the fact that exactly the same changes in aminoacid metabolism occurred in the inositol protected cells as in unprotected ones. As far as aminoacid oxidation was concerned, even drying in inositol at 70 per cent RH resulted in oxidation rates much lower than the controls (Webb, 1961).

We assumed, therefore, that a malfunction in the cell's ability to utilize glucose possibly led to a shortage of ATP. Experiments on succinate oxidation showed essentially the same trends as those utilizing glucose as a substrate, so we next followed the rate of glucose oxidation with respect to time, using cells dried at different levels of RH. Above 70 per cent RH or at lower RH levels, if inositol was present, no appreciable effect on respiration could be demonstrated; however, at the lower humidities, in the absence of inositol, respiration increased during the first fifteen minutes then rapidly decreased (Fig. 3-1). This rapid glucose oxidation by the dried cells suggested to us that the cells were attempting to effect repairs and failing. The question was — what kind of repairs? Since it did not appear to be membrane repair it could only be the synthesis of some vital component and naturally our thoughts turned to the synthesis of enzymes.

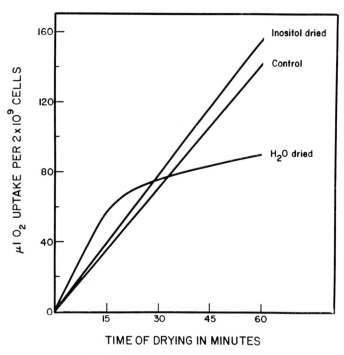

Figure 3-1 The effect of inositol on the oxidation of glucose by *S. marcescens* air-dried at 30 per cent relative humidity.

### The Synthesis of Protein and Nucleic Acids

Our first experiments concerned themselves with the production of constitutive enzymes. Cells were dried with and without inositol at 30 per cent RH for one hour and then incubated in an aminoacid-glucose medium for one hour at 37°C., sedimented by centrifugation, washed in phosphate buffer, sonically disrupted, and filtered through a millipore filter. The filtrate was then examined for various enzyme activities. In some cases, the quantity of enzyme present in the dried cells equalled that of the controls or inositol dried cells, in others it was considerably lower. This posed the problem as to whether the drying actually destroyed some of the enzymes or whether the ability of the cell to manufacture certain enzymes was impaired. Since we had examined mostly Kreb and glycolyctic enzymes, it seemed unreasonable that drying had destroyed them as they could all be isolated in an active form from cells using treatments considerably more damaging than simply drying, so we turned our attention to synthesis of the adaptive enzyme $\beta$-galactosidase. To do this, cells of *E. coli* B were grown in a medium consisting of 1.0 per cent casamino acids in 0.1M phosphate buffer and either 2.0 per cent glucose or 2.0 per cent lactose. After drying and washing, approximately 1 x $10^{10}$ cells were sonically disrupted and $\beta$-galactosidase activity in the filtrates measured using the spectrophotometric method with o-nitrophenol $\beta$-D galactopyranoside (O.N.P.G.). Others were placed in the above growth medium containing lactose incubated at 37°C. and aliquots of the cells removed at various times, sonically disrupted, filtered and enzyme activity measured. In a second series of experiments, the cells were transferred to Warburg flasks and the respiration of lactose measured. The results from both sets of experiments were essentially the same except that the presence of $\beta$-galactosidase could be detected much earlier by the spectrophotometric method than by the manometric respiration measurements. As can be seen in Fig. 3-2, some forty minutes of incubation is required before any oxygen uptake is measureable with the unadapted, glucose grown control or inositol protected dried cells, but in Fig. 3-3, the enzyme is detectable after only ten minutes. Drying at 30 per cent RH posed a problem because no enzyme synthesis could be detected even after three hours of incubation and this proved to be due to the very low viability of the cells. To overcome this difficulty, we first tried short drying periods of up to five minutes and concentrating the cells by centrifugation, and then we decided that the best approach was to utilize an RH level of 50 per cent, dry for one hour and use double the quantity of water-dried cells.

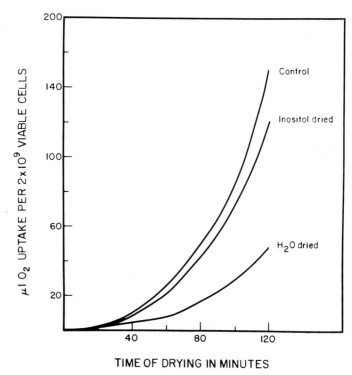

**TIME OF DRYING IN MINUTES**

Figure 3-2 The effect of inositol and drying at 50 per cent RH on the oxidation of lactose by *E. coli B* grown with glucose as a carbon source prior to drying.

In this way, we were able to use equal numbers of viable cells. The latter technique was used for the results shown in Fig. 3-2 and Fig. 3-3. It is pertinent to note at this point that in our original paper on this topic (Webb, 1961), the early increase in $\beta$-galactosidase activity was not detected with O.N.P.G., also, we had a relatively high basal enzyme activity in our "unadapted" cells. The former was due, undoubtedly, to permeability factors as it is well known that the permeability of *E. coli* to O.N.P.G. is very low. Also, at the onset of incubation in lactose, the sugar is only slowly taken up (Webb, 1963). At the time of the above experimentation, we did not possess equipment to disrupt cells and it is quite clear from our recent work (Webb, Cook and

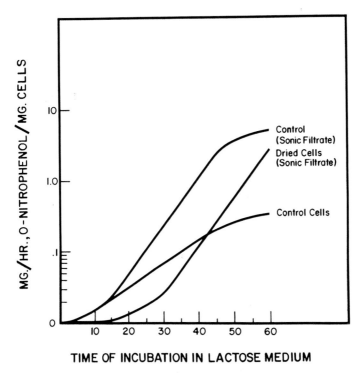

**TIME OF INCUBATION IN LACTOSE MEDIUM**

Figure 3-3 The effect of drying at 50 per cent RH on the ability of *E. coli* to manufacture adaptive β-galactosidase.

Bather, 1964) and the results presented above (Fig. 3-3) that cell permeability has a very strong influence on the enzyme rate of reaction. However, it is also apparent from both the early and recent work that the drying of the adapted cells almost completely destroys this permeability barrier whether or not inositol is there to protect the cells, as the enzyme rates obtained with these dried cells are almost equal to those obtained from the sonic filtrates of cells (Table 3-II). The high basal enzyme activity in our earlier experiments was later found to be due partly to the Tryptose medium used at that time and partly due to the strain of *E. coli*. This difficulty was overcome by changing both the medium and cell strain. In more recent work, a thymine requiring mutant of *E. coli* was used for β-galactosidase synthesis experiments and we were surprised to find that the whole set of phenomena described above could be obtained in a medium devoid of thymine. This point will be taken up later in the text.

TABLE 3-II

THE ACTIVITY OF β-GALACTOSIDASE IN DRIED AND NON-DRIED CELLS OF *Escherichia coli*

| *Treatment* | | *Non-dried* | $H_2O$ *dried (50 RH)* | *Inositol dried (50 RH)* |
|---|---|---|---|---|
| *Growth Conditions* | | | | |
| Lactose | C | 0.68* | 4.8 | 4.6 |
| grown | S | nil | 0.5 | 0.7 |
| | L | 5.4 | 5.1 | 5.8 |
| Glucose | C | nil | nil | nil |
| grown | S | nil | nil | nil |
| | L | nil | nil | nil |
| Glucose grown+ | C | 0.2 | 2.8 | 2.8 |
| 45 min. in | S | nil | 0.1 | 0.1 |
| lactose medium | L | 2.1 | 2.7 | 2.4 |

C = Cells.
S = Supernatant of cells when washed.
L = Sonic Lysate.
* = Rate expressed in mg./hr., O-nitrophenol/mg. cells.

The results indicated once more that permeability changes, as such, had little to do with cell death. The long incubation times required before β-galactosidase activity was apparent with whole cells was because of the slow penetration of both lactose and O.N.P.G. into the cell or perhaps to the synthesis of an adaptive permease considered essential by some workers. The ten-fold difference in the enzyme rate of reaction (Fig. 3-3) between whole cells and their sonic lysate after a forty-five minute adaptation period certainly indicates that the permeability of lactose and O.N.P.G. is controlled. However, the fact that β-galactosidase appeared in the sonic lysate of control cells after only ten minutes of incubation in lactose and some fifteen minutes in the dried cells suggested to us that the entry of only one or two molecules of the sugar was necessary to commence induction and once the first enzyme molecules were formed the permease synthesis followed. It was interesting to find that drying appeared to affect only the rate at which the first molecules were made as it was clear that the slope of the line during the exponential phase of enzyme synthesis was the same for both dried and non-dried cells. Apparently drying lengthened the time required for the exponential phase to be reached. Since desiccation alone increased the permeability of cells the delay in enzyme synthesis could not be correlated with the need to manufacture an induced permease but seemed to be associated with the repair of the mechanism governing protein synthesis. The increase in permeability of non-dried cells after induction, in this instance, seemed to be due to a structural change in the membrane directly resulting from the presence of lactose in the cell, as presumably lactose must first enter the cell before it can induce the synthesis of any enzyme.

Considerable time was spent studying this enzyme system, mainly because of technical troubles with our drying and the lack of cell breaking equipment. However, we finally overcame our difficulties as described, and concluded that drying delayed or completely prevented the synthesis of adaptive enzymes, a phenomenon prevented by inositol. Moreover, it was clear that desiccation did not destroy the activity of an enzyme once it was formed and this explained our earlier results with what we had considered to be constitutive enzymes, for it now seemed highly likely that many of the glycolyctic and krebs cycle enzymes were themselves adaptive, relying on the presence of their substrate, and such a thought seemed to explain the delay in the lag phase of growth of desiccated cells observed by Maltmann, Orr and Hilton (1960). Later, several other adaptive enzyme systems were examined, including the anaerobic formic hydrogenlyase. In every case, the induction process was slowed or prevented by desiccation unless inositol was added to preserve the cells.

It now seemed clear that inositol preserved the biological integrity of metabolites concerned in protein synthesis, and since it was already known that RNA viruses could be similarly protected, (Chapter 1), damage to cell RNA was indicated as the reason for death. Naturally, our first thought centered around permeability factors and we theorized that inositol prevented the leakage of RNA from the dried cells. Our illusions, however, were quickly shattered when we discovered that far from leakage prevention, inositol or drying at high humidities above 70 per cent, where cells survived well, actually increased the release of 260 m$\mu$ absorbing material which on hydrolysis and chromatographic analysis yielded the four bases of RNA. Moreover, this RNA was relatively free from protein (Fig. 3-4). It could only be assumed, in the light of these findings, and those with enzymes, that permeability changes resulting in the release of cell materials were non-lethal, in fact the retention of RNA seemed to be involved in the death mechanism. Thus, it was necessary to turn our attention to the synthesis of nucleic acids and protein by dried cells. This we did by following the uptake of $C^{14}$ labelled aminoacids, uracil and thymine.

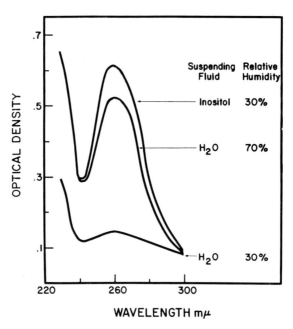

Figure 3-4 The effect of drying at 30 per cent and 70 per cent RH and inositol treatment on the ultraviolet spectra of cell supernatant fluids.

In these experiments, a thymine deficient strain of *E. coli* was used because little thymine uptake could be obtained with the prototrophic organism. As the protected cells had lost much of their RNA, it was felt that the synthesis of the latter by protected cells would be more rapid than non-dried controls. This proved to be a false assumption for RNA synthesis was, in fact, slower than the controls during the first fifteen minutes of incubation. The unprotected cells displayed a very rapid rate of uracil incorporation during the same fifteen-minute period and then the rate slowed to that of the controls. This rapid incorporation of uracil was not accompanied by an equal increase in the rate of aminoacid or thymine uptake, both of which proved to be considerably delayed.

Since the uptakes had been calculated on the basis of an equal number of viable cells (approximately $10^7$), we could only assume that the rapid uracil incorporation went on in dying cells and this over-activity led to their death. Thus, the retention of damaged RNA appeared to be lethal and it seemed plausible that such a phenomenon could interfere with the synthesis of DNA polymerase and other enzymes. One action of inositol, therefore, seemed to be to allow the exit of damaged RNA and another to preserve the integrity of that which remained in the cell.

At this point of our investigations, we imagined we had solved the problem, then we began to wonder what caused the delay in aminoacid and thymine uptake, and why was this only noticeable during the first fifteen minutes of incubation following treatment? Also, why was the DNA unable to effect RNA repairs by manufacturing new messenger RNA? The loss of the ability of a dried cell to manufacture adaptive enzymes, and possibly respiratory enzymes, became difficult to reconcile with the current ideas of protein synthesis via messenger RNA unless the DNA was damaged also by the desiccation process, but up to this point there had been no indication of such an occurrence.

We decided, therefore, to look further into the relationships between DNA, RNA, and protein, and after many experiments trying various RH levels and drying times, we finally found we could get reproducible results if we allowed the cells to reach equilibrium at 50 per cent RH and dry them for fifteen minutes only. In this way, very few cells died and we could follow the sequences of repair by tracer uptake experiments. Some control cells were allowed to dry at 80 per cent RH for the same length of time others were allowed to starve in 0.1 m phosphate buffer

instead of drying. The results of these two later sets of experiments were remarkable in that they suggested again that two
phases of both RNA and protein synthesis existed in these microbial cells and that desiccation under the described conditions only
affected the first phase. Moreover, DNA synthesis did not occur
until Phase I was completed which took about fifteen minutes in
controls and up to thirty minutes in cells dried without inositol
(Fig. 3-5).

A definite amount of RNA and protein synthesis appeared to
be necessary before the DNA could replicate for no matter how

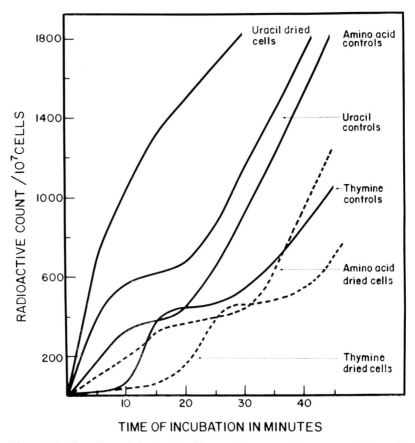

**TIME OF INCUBATION IN MINUTES**

Figure 3-5 The effect of drying for fifteen minutes at 50 per cent RH on the
uptake of $C^{14}$ labelled metabolites by *E. coli*. Control cells dried at 80 per
cent RH or held in 0.1M phosphate buffer for fifteen minutes.

long phase 1 took in any of our non-dried controls or in dried
cells where few deaths occurred, the amount of uracil and amino
acids taken up always reached the same level before any thymine
incorporation was detectable. The only difference between the
water-dried and inositol-dried cells was that uracil incorporation
by inositol protected cells was always slower in phase 1, and we
took this as indicating that inositol could replace uracil in some
way (Fig. 3-6). This assumption was based on the fact that, of
the RNA released by inositol after drying, the greatest proportion
of it was uracil and cytosine with 18 per cent to 20 per cent of the
cell's uracil being displaced (Webb, Cook and Bather, 1964). Drying at 80 per cent RH also resulted in RNA release and starvation
is known to render the ribosomal RNA inactive or bring about its
degradation. These points, therefore, suggested to us that phase 1
was a process under the control of the DNA which resulted in the
manufacture of messenger RNA and some proteins, but was
necessary for DNA replication. However, since adaptive enzymes
in control cells appeared during this early stage some enzyme
molecules must have been manufactured before the messenger
RNA reached the ribosomes, and indeed, before the DNA repli-
cated. The latter phenomenon was checked with the thymine
requiring mutant of *E. coli,* and in a medium deficient of thymine
the two phased uptake of aminoacids and uracil was observed, and
also the synthesis of $\beta$-galactosidase occurred just as it had done
with the prototrophic organism. Obviously, in this case, DNA
replication was not required for adaptive enzyme or RNA
synthesis.

The delay in uracil uptake by inositol protected dried cells
now became more readily explainable. If we assumed that inositol
displaced the messenger RNA from ribosomes, and the same was
true for starvation or drying at 80 per cent RH, then no cytoplasmic RNA synthesis would occur until new messenger RNA
had been manufactured. This hypothesis was rendered more
plausible when the composition of the RNA released from tumor
cells by inositol suggested it to be single stranded RNA analogous
to messenger RNA (Bather, Webb and Sebastian, 1964). Both
the topic of this early protein synthesis and the animal cell experi-

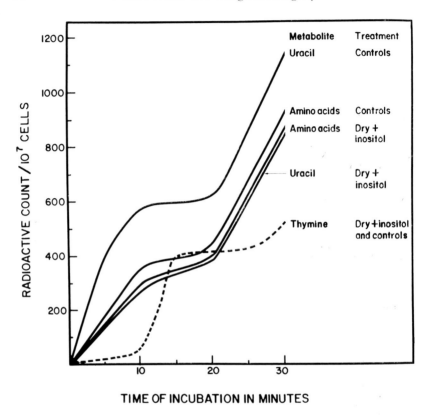

Figure 3-6 The effect of inositol on the incorporation of labelled metabolites
by *E. coli* air-dried for fifteen minutes at 50 per cent RH.

ments will be taken up again in later chapters, and suffice to say
here that these observations stimulated the radiation and animal
cell work to be described in these chapters.

Naturally, we were intrigued by the apparent two phases of
protein and RNA synthesis and the effect of drying on them, as
well as the ability of inositol to slow down uracil uptake. In a
recent series of experiments, we examined the effect of adding 5
per cent inositol to a full growth medium and to a minimal
medium (MM) on the uptake of thymine, uracil and individual
aminoacids. These experiments demonstrated that, in MM
especially, the uptake of uracil during the first fifteen minutes was

slowed, and so was the incorporation of alanine, arginine, lysine, leucine, and thymine. Of the aminoacids tested, arginine uptake appeared the most affected. However, the addition of 5 per cent inositol to a full medium appeared to increase the burst size of virus infected cells while the stability of the formed phages to irradiation, desiccation or on storage in liquids increased. These findings suggest that inositol is able to take the place of some aminoacids on the DNA molecule, possibly by attaching itself to the $=P=O$ or $=C=O$ groups, and without activation by phosphorylated RNA bases. It was now necessary to find out whether or not the cell DNA was damaged by desiccation and two methods seemed open to us. One was to look for the production of mutant cells and the other was to test the ability of *E. coli* to manufacture bacteriophages after drying, and it was the second choice we first examined.

### The Effects of Bound Water Loss on the Synthesis and Release of Viruses

The ability of dried cells to synthesize coliphage T2 was first examined and to our surprise we found "dead" cells quite capable of virus manufacture. Even when the cells were dried at 30 per cent RH where less than 1.0 per cent of them were capable of colony formation, on infection with T2 they produced an equal number of virus particles as the controls. To us this meant that, (a) the enzymes necessary for T2 synthesis were intact; (b) the synthesis of the phage specific enzymes was not affected by the drying of host cells, and (c) the overactive RNA synthesis observed earlier in dried cells did not prevent the normal biological activity of, at least, phage DNA. Later, when uracil uptake was measured in dried cells infected with T2 phage, only a very low uracil uptake was detectable so apparently phage infection even stopped the damaged RNA from functioning. This phenomenon was studied again later when radiation experiments were conducted and for the sake of continuity I shall defer further comment on this topic until chapter four. Coliphage T2 does not require the host DNA to be intact, but many workers have reported that T3 and T7 phages do, so we repeated our experiments with these two phages.

In our aerosol impinger samples, we collected about 2 x $10^6$ cells/ ml., these we concentrated by centrifugation into 2.0 ml. of HIB broth and 2.0 ml. of a phage suspension containing approximately 1 x $10^7$ phage particles/ml. was added. A 1.0 ml. aliquot was removed for phage count immediately, and a second after two hours of incubation at 30°C. Aerosol samples were collected at zero time and after sixty minutes of storage in air. Several RH levels were studied as well as the effect of inositol at 30 per cent RH. With both phages a reduced ability of the host cell to support their growth was found if the cells were held at humidity levels below 65 per cent, but the reduction in phage producing "capacity" was not as great as the loss of viability (Fig. 3-7).

As with other cell properties inositol completely prevented this loss in phage producing capacity. The next question we posed was what would happen to the virus, once inside the cell, if the

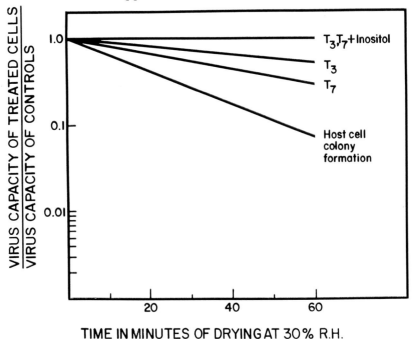

TIME IN MINUTES OF DRYING AT 30% R.H.

Figure 3-7 The ability of *E. coli* B to manufacture T3 and T7 coliphages after various periods of drying at 30 per cent RH with and without inositol.

infected cell was aerosolised. To do this required a slight change in our techniques, for it was necessary to have a cell concentration of about $2 \times 10^9$ in our aerosol spray suspension and we needed to get most of them infected and aerosolised within a short period of time. By using logarithmically growing host *E. coli B* and high speed centrifugation we managed to concentrate the viruses to the desired level. Also, we could not aerosolize from distilled water as phage absorption possibly would not take place, instead we added 1.0 ml of a 0.5 per cent solution of casamino acids containing 0.1 per cent glucose to the suspension before aerosolization. Tests on the stability of cells aerosolized from such a solution showed the decay rate to be only slightly less than those of water aerosolized cells. A relative humidity of 30 per cent was used for these tests in order to obtain maximum effects. The collected aerosol samples were plated on plates seeded with *E. coli B* and plaque counts recorded. It took four minutes to establish the aerosol so we could only compare the happenings after a six-minute infection period, but as it turned out, this did not affect our results. With T7 virus, the plaque forming ability showed the same decay rate as the host cell if the infected cells were aerosolized within six minutes after infection. When cells were aerosolised after this period, however, the plaque forming ability greatly increased and at about fifteen minutes little or no reduction was found (Fig. 3-8). Oddly enough, the virus itself was found to be very susceptible to aerosolization but it too was stabilized with inositol as were other cells and viruses. Phages T2 and T3 behaved likewise in that plaque formation increased as the time of infection before aerosolization increased although the magnitudes of the effects differed. Moreover, this reduction in plaque forming ability at the early stages of infection due to drying was prevented by inositol.

These findings intrigued us greatly and it was a natural follow-up to examine the behaviour of a lysogenic organism actually carrying a latent virus. The organism chosen was *E. coli K. 12* kindly supplied to us by Dr. G. S. Stent of the University of California. Initial experiments on its aerosol stability at 30 per cent RH indicated it to be more sensitive than *E. coli B* and we began to suspect that the aerosolization procedure induced the cell to liberate its lambda phage. The aerosol samples were collected, therefore, in 0.1 per cent glucose and 2.0 ml. of nutrient broth added. A 1.0 ml. aliquot was immediately filtered through a millipore filter, the filtrate diluted and plated on seeded plates of a lambda phage sensitive strain of *E. coli,* again supplied to us by Dr. Stent. The rest of the sample was incubated for two hours, filtered, and phage counts made. The results were remarkable in that drying did induce the K12 cell to liberate its phage and the number of cells induced to do so depended both on the relative humidity and the time of storage in the air. In later work the treated or untreated cells were incubated for 30 minutes only and then plated onto seeded plates. This allowed the number of cells undergoing lysis to be directly determined. There was little or no release of phage from cells aerosolised at 90 per cent RH. To analyse the results further we irradiated cells for ten seconds with ultraviolet light UV. The concentration of cells used was the same as that collected at zero time in our aerosol samples and the dilution necessary was made from a suspension of cells prepared for aerosolization. Cell and virus counts were made before irradiation and again two hours after treatment. A second sample was treated likewise but without irradiation. In this way, we were able to determine a burst size and the number of viruses produced during the two hour incubation period without drying or ultraviolet light. As a check, an aliquot of each collected aerosol sample was filtered and assayed for virus before the two hour incubation period and in no case were we able to detect any virus. Using the burst size obtained we calculated the percentage of the cells induced to liberate phage and the percentage induced in our non-aerosolized control. Having done this, we plotted our results using the ratio:

$$\frac{\text{Percentage dry cells induced}}{\text{Percentage control cells induced}}\text{versus time in the aerosol (Fig.}$$

3-9). In the controls, the percentage of cells liberating virus ranged from 0.002 to 0.007 per cent and in the aerosols from 0.02 to 10.1 per cent, the latter 10.1 per cent was obtained

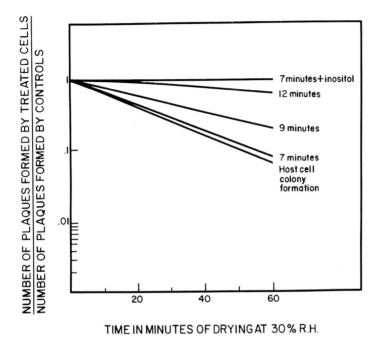

TIME IN MINUTES OF DRYING AT 30% R.H.

Figure 3-8 The effect of post-infection time on the sensitivity of intra-cellular T2 vegetative phage toward desiccation at 30 per cent RH and the protective action of inositol.

from water-dried cells at 30 per cent RH after an hour of drying. On a percentage cell/virus basis, it was clear that drying at humidities below 70 per cent induced far more cells than desiccation above this RH level (Webb, Dumasia and Singh, 1964). In addition, it was evident that inositol stopped induction at 30 per cent RH as well as at 70 per cent RH. In Chapter 1, Fig. 1-4, it was shown that at about 70 per cent RH only water bound directly to macromolecules remains and these are part of the structure of the molecule. At humidities above 80 per cent multi-layers of water are formed and it seemed logical that inositol, because of its structure, could act as a water "block" something akin to that described by Klotz (1958). If such is the case, then the "prophage" appears to be affixed to the host DNA through water-

water hydrogen bonds, and if these water molecules are kept in place it will replicate along with the host DNA.

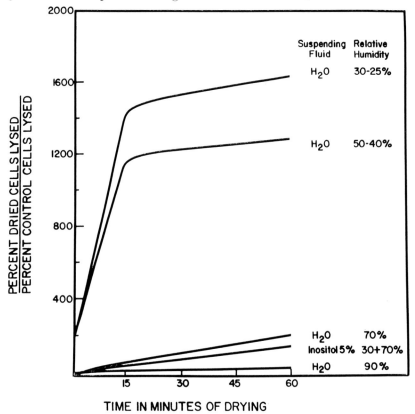

Figure 3-9 The effect of RH and inositol on cell lysis and the synthesis of Lambda phage by semi-dried cells of *E. coli K12*.

The amount of lysis even at low humidities accounted for only a small part of the higher death rates noted with *E. coli* K12 over that of other coli strains. For instance, assuming we normally collected 20 x $10^5$ cells/ml. in our impinger samples, a 10.0 per cent extra loss would result in a count of 18 x $10^5$, and this was well within our normal aerosol experimental error, so there had to be another cause. In the lysogenic induction experiments, we had pre-incubated our cells for two hours in fresh medium, then resuspended in water or inositol for aerosolization; in other words, the cells had just reached the end of the lag phase or just entered logarithmic growth. A reasonable deduction then was that as the cells progressed through the lag phase they became progressively more susceptible to desiccation damage. This we examined by re-suspending the washed cells in a weak medium of aminoacids and glucose, as had been done with the T phage experiments, and aerosolized them at different incubation times. The results were contrary to expectation as during the first ten minutes the cells became more resistant then suddenly their desiccation sensitivity increased by almost a factor of two. Following this, a gradual decline took place until a death rate was reached comparable to that found when cells were aerosolized while in the logarithmic phase of growth (Fig. 3-10). To find out if this reflected the physical state of the host DNA we again checked the virus "capacity" but

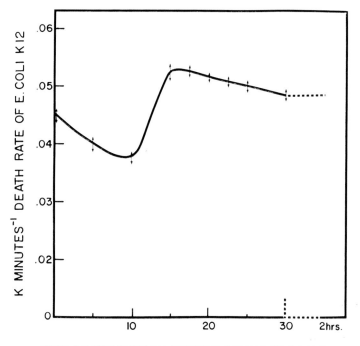

TIME OF INCUBATION BEFORE DRYING AT 30% R.H.

Figure 3-10 The influence of incubation time during the lag period of growth and prior to aerosolization on the sensitivity of *E. coli K12* to drying at 30 per cent RH.

this time with cells pre-incubated for a given time before aerosolization. The results in Table 3-III indicated that at least part of the increase in death rate was due to DNA damage and it was interesting to find that the ratio capacity/colony formation remained relatively constant, regardless of incubation time, and had approximate values of three, six, and four for T1, T3 and T7 respectively.

TABLE 3-III

THE EFFECT OF INCUBATION TIME ON THE "CAPACITY" OF DRIED *E. coli B* TO MANUFACTURE SEVERAL VIRUSES

| Phage | Time of Incubation | | | | |
|---|---|---|---|---|---|
| | 0 | 5 | 10 | 15 | 30 |
| T2 | 1.0* | 0.9 | 1.2 | 0.8 | 1.3 |
| T4 | 1.1 | 0.8 | 1.2 | 1.1 | 0.8 |
| T1 | 0.2 | 0.3 | 0.4 | 0.1 | 0.2 |
| T3 | 0.5 | 0.6 | 0.8 | 0.2 | 0.4 |
| T7 | 0.3 | 0.4 | 0.6 | 0.1 | 0.2 |
| Colony formation of cells. | 0.08 | 0.10 | 0.15 | 0.03 | 0.06 |

\* = Results expressed as ratio $\dfrac{\text{No. of infected cells}}{\text{No. of plagues produced}}$

The cells were collected after one hour of drying at 30 percent RH, infected with the appropriate phage and after an incubation time of ten minutes they were diluted and plated on seeded plates of *E. coli B*. A second uninfected sample was plated for cell counts.

At this stage of our work, we now knew that desiccation of a bacterial cell in aerosols at certain RH levels affected its ability to manufacture a virus and would induce the release of a temperate phage. In later experiments, this was found to be true also for animal cells (Chapter 5). As far as inositol was concerned, it seemed to prevent this inactivation of the cell's virus "capacity" as far as T7 and T3 phages were concerned, stopped the loss of ability to synthesize adaptive enzymes and prevented the induction of phage from lysogenic *E. coli K12*. On the other hand, it did not prevent the release of enzymes, aminoacids or nucleic acids from dried cells. According to Kornberg (1960) and Flak *et al.* (1959), various phage specific enzymes are manufactured during the early stages of T2 infection and since the infected cell lost its ability to produce phage only if it was desiccated within ten minutes after infection it was easy to reason that these enzymes, once formed, were stable to drying and capable of manufacturing virus. If this was true then the integrity of the viral DNA must have been preserved by inositol for it prevented any effects of drying. The fact that the host cell increased in stability during this early period, while the phage showed maximal sensitivity indicated that some relationship between the "early proteins" and the structure or replication of DNA was responsible. In any event, in the absence of inositol, dried cells could not readily synthesize adaptive enzymes but could manufacture T2 virus and to some extent T3 and T7 viruses and this suggested that DNA damage due to drying did occur. The logic we had applied to form the hypotheses of RNA protection by inositol no longer seemed to apply, for it is well known that RNA synthesis stops on infection with a bacteriophage, and unless one supposed cell RNA to be necessary for viral DNA replication, the only conclusion seemed to be that inositol preserved the integrity of not only RNA but also of DNA. Why then was the viral DNA more stable after the initial synthesis of protein? This stability could hardly be due to the hardiness of DNA polymerase or the other phage specific enzymes because if this were true then the host cell should behave likewise for presumably its polymerases should be manufactured during the same early periods in its growth cycle, yet the cell showed a gradual increase in stability followed by a decrease. The polymerase hypothesis, therefore, did not seem to hold true and we were forced to examine more closely the two phases of protein synthesis found earlier and to try and find out what happened to them on infection with bacteriophage.

Our findings were in no way contradictory to those of other workers. RNA synthesis in terms of $C^{14}$ uptake was small and so was protein synthesis. However, viewed in terms of what happened to uninfected cells the results were more meaningful for the secondary uracil uptake was completely prevented. More remarkable still was the finding that all stages of RNA and protein synthesis as well as $\beta$-galactosidase induction occurred in the absence of thymine with the uninfected T- strain of *E. coli*. These results could not be reconciled with the current ideas of DNA action. Apparently, replication of DNA was not required for it to code RNA and protein, yet obviously from the previous data the early

uptake of aminoacids and uracil represented happenings controlled by DNA. The secondary stage of protein and RNA synthesis was assumed, therefore, to be a protein-RNA cycle going on
completely independently of the DNA. Thus induction required
the DNA code whereas the synthesis of so called constitutive
enzymes and some RNA relied on pre-coded RNA in the cell. It
was now easy to reason that if this pre-coded RNA was damaged
and retained by the cell, death could result from the build up of
deformed RNA, but if it was shed from the cell new RNA could
be coded from DNA provided the latter remained undamaged.
This hypothesis seemed to explain all the observed happenings
such as death, loss of ability to produce T3 and T7 phages and
adaptive enzymes, but it did not explain why the viral DNA was
so desiccation sensitive at the onset of infection or the increased
sensitivity of the host cell during the period of rapid DNA replication. Therefore, we could only assume that DNA damage was
more likely to occur with molecules devoid of a protein coat or
in the single stranded (or open) state.

   In an attempt to resolve this problem we obtained T2 viruses
heavily labelled with $C^{14}$ algae protein hydrolysate aminoacids,
infected *E. coli B* in a cold medium, sonically disrupted them after
five minutes and after centrifugation and filtration to remove cell
walls and whole cells, attempted to trace the label in various components of the sonic lysate. The cold TCA precipitate was electro-
phorised and the position of any labelling determined. In a second
series of experiments, cells labelled with both Uracil $C^{14}$ and $C^{14}$
amino acid were infected with a "cold" phage and the sonic lysate
treated likewise. In the former case, several labelled bands were
obtained apparently associated with components absorbing at 260
$m\mu$. In the second case a cold band of protein was found associated
with a hot RNA band. However, the purification and isolation of
these complexes proved difficult as they were numerous and easily
dissociated by such things as NaCl extraction. The existence of
labelled "nucleoproteins" after hot $C^{14}$ protein phage infection
and the apparent association of cold phage protein with "hot"
cell RNA suggested to us that perhaps the "internal" protein of
T2 phage attached itself to not only host DNA but also to host

RNA and thus brought host RNA synthesis to a halt, but why the internal protein should separate from the viral DNA was not at the time, an easy question to answer, even by speculation.

At this point of our investigations, we felt the pursuit of the above topic was a full time one which perhaps someone would like to take up. We were convinced now that desiccation did affect DNA structure and function and to examine this from a different standpoint we began to look into the possibility of desiccation being mutagenic.

## The Mutagenic Action of Bound Water Loss

It was indeed fortunate for me that my good friend and technician Mr. R. Hodges had noticed repeatedly in experiments with *Serratia marcescens* that white mutants appeared under certain conditions of drying and had kept a careful record of them during some five years of work. Such observations now assumed much importance and as we went over the records we were delighted to find that relative humidity played an important role in the production of these mutants and that inositol appeared to completely suppress them. To attack this problem further, we first looked for Lac⁻ mutants of our Lac⁺ strain grown in Glucose-amino acid medium but without success. Then we decided to plate our cells on minimal medium as well as a full medium to see whether agar overlays containing amino acids would allow more cells to replicate. In every case, fewer cells developed on the minimal medium than on the full medium but mutants were hard to come by. Therefore, we reviewed the situation and realizing that to find color mutants hundreds of plates had been examined our technique was changed and two methods employed. The aerosol samples were collected in minimal medium containing 200 $\mu$g of penicillin/ml. These were incubated for four hours at 37°C, and the cells sedimented by centrifugation, washed in saline, resuspended in 1.0 ml of Saline, plated onto minimal medium agar and the cells allowed to grow for 18 hours. The plates were then photographed and an overlay of amino acids applied. In the second technique, penicillin was not used, instead we used large petri dishes on which from 1000 to 2000 discrete colonies could form. Each technique allowed us to examine thousands of cells relatively quickly, to isolate potential mutants and by comparing the two sets of results make a fairly accurate determination of mutant numbers. In no case with aminoacid deficient mutants did we determine the precise blockages as this was not pertinent to our studies. Above 70 per cent RH or with inositol at low humidities few mutants were found but the water dried cells produced up to 200 per $10^6$ survivors, and the maximum number occurred when drying was carired out at 40 per cent RH (Webb, 1964). Attempts to isolate Lac⁻ cells, however, failed even though the technique of using Lactose⁻ E.M.B. agar was much more simple than the overlays. The two sets of experiments were apparently contradictory. One could obtain one sort of mutant but not another and it seemed unrealistic to suppose we had found a differential method of mutant production, and illogical that one gene was more sensitive to desiccation than another. What then could be the cause? After much brain searching, we realized that some aminoacids, sugars and pyrimidenes were protective to airborne cells as well as inositol, and we wondered whether the constitutive enzyme or coded RNA formed before drying protected the genes. The RNA was dismissed because we knew it to be badly affected, this left the enzyme which appeared unaffected by drying. Why should an enzyme protect a gene? We had no idea, but it was a relatively simple matter to find out if cells having all their genes in operation were more or less stable to desiccation. This we did by growing *E. coli* in a liquid minimal medium containing 0.25% $(NH_4)_2SO_4$ or $NH_4Cl$; 1.0 per cent glucose in O.IM $NaH_2PO_4$ + $K_2HPO_4$ buffer pH 7.0. No NaCl was added and tap water was used to supply the essential trace elements. Good growth was obtained on this medium. Washed cells grown in the above manner proved to be more stable to drying and the number of aminoacid mutants was considerably smaller, again no Lac⁻ mutants were found and so we came to the remarkable conclusion that preformed enzymes other than DNA polymerase must stabilize a gene. However, we were not happy with this conclusion because many workers have tried to carry over genetic information via proteins and failed. Also, so much evidence has accumulated for the role of DNA in genetic continuity that we were left only with doubts as to the method by which the DNA functioned in coding RNA and protein. The thought arose, therefore, that it was not the enzymes that protected gene sites but the metabolites themselves, growth in media containing aminoacids did not stop dependent organisms from occurring but growth on a minimal medium did. This idea led us to examine the behaviour of cells dried as a slurry, i.e., in the medium in which they were grown. The results were remarkable in that under such conditions cells in minimal medium were almost as stable as washed cells to which inositol had been added, moreover, no mutants were obtained. Also, if the minimal medium supernatant obtained after the growth of cells was added to washed, rich medium grown cells considerable protection was afforded them (Table 3-IV). It was clear, therefore, that the metabolites themselves were responsible for the protection of both viability and genetic continuity and that their position in the cell was very important. Since they could be washed from the cell relatively weak associations were indicated possibly through bonds similar to water H-bonds. The structural importance of added chemicals found in Chapter 2 now began to make sense as well as the role of inositol, for such results added support to the hypothesis that inositol was able to preserve the integrity of both DNA and RNA.

TABLE 3-IV

THE EFFECT OF GROWTH AND PLATING MEDIUM ON THE DEATH RATE OF AIR-DRIED *E. coli*

| Aerosolization Conditions | Death Rate (K)* | |
| --- | --- | --- |
| | MM (Plating) | FM (Plating) |
| FM cells in water | 0.048 | 0.042 |
| MM cells in water | 0.026 | 0.021 |
| FM cells in slurry | 0.033 | 0.028 |
| MM cells in slurry | 0.009 | 0.009 |
| FM cells in MM spent culture fluid | 0.010 | 0.012 |
| MM cells in FM spent culture fluid | 0.021 | 0.018 |
| FM cells in 5% INOSITOL | 0.006 | 0.007 |
| FM cells in 2% ARGININE | 0.018 | 0.017 |

FM Full medium, MM minimal medium.
*Death rate calculated from $N_t = N_o e^{-Kt}$

There still remained the question of why we were unable to obtain Lac⁻ mutants and the above results gave us the clue. It is well known that glucose will inhibit β-galactosidase synthesis so we assumed that glucose must bind preferentially with the same sites as lactose. Therefore, we decided to grow cells in succinate and acetate media in the hope that the genes controlling the synthesis of the glycolytic enzymes would be non functional. To dilute out coded RNA six passages in these media with small inocula were made before the experiments were carried out. The results were extremely gratifying as relatively large numbers of Lac⁻ cells were obtained using washed cells dried from water. Again their number was controlled by the bound water content of the cells and no mutant was found if inositol, glucose or lactose was added prior to drying.

In the next series of experiments, we examined the phenomenon of back mutations. First we developed strains of *E. coli* resistant to streptomycin and chloramphenicol by the gradient plate technique and plated our aerosol samples on ordinary HIB plates and also on plates containing 100 $\mu$ gms./ml. of the antibiotic to which the cells were originally resistant. In each case, cell recoveries were higher on the antibiotic free medium than on the antibiotic containing medium. However, the few isolated colonies we examined all retained their full resistance and we were left to wonder whether some cells had lost their resistance permanently or whether the presence of the antibiotic had made it difficult for some damaged cells to effect repairs. In an effort to resolve this, we incubated the cells collected from the aerosol in HIB Broth for four hours and then plated on the two kinds of media. Knowing our initial cell count on HIB agar and final count we could estimate the number of generations in the four-hour period and from the number that still refused to grow on the antibiotic containing medium calculate how many probable back mutants had occurred assuming the same mean generation time. The results indicated that "back" mutants did occur and that their occurrence followed the same RH pattern as the aminoacid and Lac⁻ mutants.

We next obtained cultures of *E. coli* requiring one of the following:— thymine; arginine; methionine and tryptophan and a streptomycin dependent organism. With these organisms the aerosol samples were collected in saline and the cells concentrated by centrifugation into 1.0 ml. One aliquot of 0.5 ml. was plated on minimal medium directly and another incubated for one hour in a 0.1 per cent mixture of aminoacids. These cells were then washed twice and plated onto minimal medium. The latter process was carried out because of the finding of Witken (1956) and Schwartz and Strauss (1958) that few if any back mutants are obtained if the treated cells are not pre-incubated in this way before plating. Our own results were in accord with these findings.

The sum total of our results are tabulated in Table 3-V. It was apparent that desiccation did produce mutants either forward or backward and that the number produced was strongly dependent

TABLE 3-V

THE EFFECT OF BOUND WATER CONTENT ON THE PRODUCTION OF BACTERIAL MUTANTS

| Mutant Type | | 30 | 40 | *Relative Humidity* 50 | 60 | 70 | 80 |
|---|---|---|---|---|---|---|---|
| White Serriatia |
| marcescens | | 316* | 342 | 404 | 204 | 1 | 2 |
| Aminoacid |
| requiring | | 62 | 173 | 120 | 15 | 0 | 0 |
| Lactose |
| negative | | 72 | 156 | 148 | 50 | 0 | 0 |
| Chloramphenicol |
| sensitive from | | 94 | 318 | 331 | 67 | 5 | 4 |
| resistance |
| Streptomycin |
| independent from | | 103 | 216 | 208 | 62 | 1 | 0 |
| streptomycin |
| dependent |
| Tryptophan |
| independent | A | 433 | 755 | 273 | 42 | 2 | 1 |
| from |
| dependent | B | 10 | 8 | 4 | 1 | 0 | 2 |
| Arginine |
| independent | A | 284 | 522 | 322 | 28 | 3 | 0 |
| from |
| dependent | B | 4 | 7 | 3 | 1 | 2 | 1 |
| Methionine |
| independent | A | 208 | 396 | 201 | 5 | 3 | 1 |
| from |
| dependent | B | 7 | 8 | 1 | 0 | 2 | 0 |

*Calculated on the basis of approximately $10^6$ viable cells.

A = Aerosolized from water.

B = Aerosolized from water plus the metabolite.

on the RH at which the cells were held. In all cases, a maximum mutant yield was obtained between 40-50 per cent RH. More important perhaps was the experimental suggestion that small molecular weight metabolites stabilized the genetic material in the cell. Cells aerosolized as a "slurry" and grown in minimal medium were not only highly stable viability-wise, but also from a genetic standpoint. Moreover, the integrity of a particular gene or genes seemed to be stabilized by the presence of the required metabolite or inositol.

These results indicated that the combination of inositol or small metabolites could prevent DNA and RNA damage. Since drying in inert gases did not change the picture appreciably, we concluded that in the absence of bound water or a protective molecule $=C=O$ or $=P=O$ groups were forming strong cross link H-bonds with $-NH_2$; $-OH$ or $-N$ groups and these bonds were irreversible with water and distorted the DNA or RNA molecules. To test this idea, we first looked for peroxides in desiccated cells and found none. Then, using the free radical $\alpha,\alpha$ diphenyl-$\beta$-picryl-hydrazyl (DPPH) (Poirer *et al.* 1952; Blois, 1958), we measured the number of free reducing groups in control, inositol protected and unprotected dried cells. The cells were dried for one hour at 30 per cent RH and an equal number sonically disrupted in saline or inositol. The sonic filtrate was centrifuged at slow speed to remove large cells wall fractions and the supernatant used for our determinations. According to Blois aromatic compounds with a single $-OH$ group only or glucose are not oxidized by DPPH whereas polyhydroxy aromatic compounds and aromatic amines, ascorbic acid and the $-SH$ groups of pro tein are oxidized. In our experiments, inositol was not oxidized by the DPPH. As can be seen from Table 3-VI, the number of free reacting groups in cells dried from water was less than half of that of the inositol protected or control cells. Since the drying was carried out in the absence of free oxygen we felt justified in saying that in the absence of bound water oxidizing and reducing groups did interact irreversibly and this was responsible for the subsequent biological malfunction of the affected molecules lead ing to mutation or death. It was noticed also that some recovery of the water-dried cells occurred if resuspended in inositol. Blois states that under "ordinary conditions" DPPH does not react with purines or pyrimidines, however, with isolated DNA or RNA we were able to obtain a reaction.

TABLE 3-VI

THE EFFECT OF DESSICCATION AND INOSITOL ON THE REDUCING GROUPS OF *E. coli* MEASURED USING THE FREE RADICAL DIPHENYL-$\beta$-PICRYLHYDRAZYL

|  | Control Cells | Inositol Dried | Water Dried |
|---|---|---|---|
| Cells disrupted in saline | 11.58 | 10.43 | 6.72 |
| Cells disrupted in inositol | 11.56 | 11.54 | 8.09 |

Results expressed as $\mu$ equiv./gm. cells.

In a final series of experiments, to examine the effect of inositol on proteins themselves we utilized as a test system the agglutination of *E. coli* by its antibody. This was simply done by drying a given quantity of the cells or antiserum on microscope slides and determining the amount of agglutination in the usual way. The results (Table 3-VII) indicated that the antigens were damaged by desiccation and inositol would partly prevent this from occurring. In addition, inositol lowered the level of agglutination in non-dried controls presumably by interfering with the action of NaCl or binding with antigenic sites. No effect of drying on the antibody, however, could be demonstrated.

TABLE 3-VII

AGGLUTINATION OF CONTROL AND DRIED *E. coli* BY ANTISERUM

| Dilution | 1/30 | 1/60 | 1/120 | 1/240 | 1/480 |
|---|---|---|---|---|---|
| Control | ++++ | ++++ | ++++ | ++++ | ++++ |
| Control and inositol | ++++ | +++ | +++ | +++ | +++ |
| Dry | +++ | ++ | + | − | − |
| Dry+ Inositol | ++++ | +++ | +++ | +++ | ++ |

## Summary and Conclusions

As with the work described in the previous chapters, we had tried to conduct our experiments in some sort of logical sequence based on hypotheses from experimental results. This type of approach led us directly into the mechanisms of protein synthesis and problems of genetic continuity not only of bacterial cells but also of animal cells.

Many technical problems were encountered particularly in the drying of cells on filters and it is easy for me to visualize some of the troubles of other workers with drying techniques. Unless one uses extremely thin films of cells the drying rate is slow and desiccation is often incomplete due to the protection of upper layers of dead or dying cells. This phenomenon makes it absolutely necessary to check cell counts before and after drying because, as was mentioned in the text, under some conditions protective agents such as inositol become toxic. This never occurs in the aerosol and it was for this reason that wherever possible the aerosol was used as the means of desiccation.

The study of protein, nucleic acid synthesis and genetic continuity through the effects of drying is an unusual one but, in the light of our findings, nevertheless a valid one. There seems to be no doubt that the enzymes of a cell existing prior to desiccation are still able to function even to the point of manufacturing viruses and so the lethal action of partial drying could hardly be ascribed to the inactivation of enzymes. In addition, any permeability change allowing the leakage of cell material seems desirable rather than lethal and this appears particularly true for some kinds of animal cells. Such an observation is not too surprizing as it is well known that enzymes, RNA and various other metabolites are shed from actively growing cells. Often this is a preamble to sporulation or dormancy, a state in which cells are particularly stable to many physical agents, and contain a low level of water.

Two reasons for cell death were apparent and both involved the synthesis of new metabolites or rather the enzymes necessary for their synthesis, damage to RNA undoubtedly occurred and produced a rapid uptake of uracil by dead or dying cells. This could well lead to the death of a cell due to an incorrect RNA/DNA balance akin to that found responsible for the death of thymine requiring cells grown on a thymine deficient medium (Cohen and Barner, 1954) and because of the stabilization of Rous sarcoma virus by inositol a reasonable assumption appeared to be that some cell protection by this compound resulted from the prevention of RNA damage. However, the ability of inositol to keep the T3 and T7 phage producing capacity of a cell intact during drying and to prevent the inactivation of T2 and other viruses during the early stages of their developement in a cell as well as its demonstrated ability to prevent mutations strongly suggested that the removal of bound water also affects cell DNA. Such an assumption was rendered more plausible by the work of Falk, Hartman and Lord (1963) who, by means of infra-red spectroscopy were able to show that the structure of DNA does rely on the correct positioning of bound water molecules. These workers found that between aproximately 70 and 50 per cent RH, water molecules bound to the $-NH$, $-N$, and $-OH$ groups are removed and at lower humidities those attached to the $=C=O$ and $=P=O$ are affected. It would thus seem to be more than just coincidence that these are the precise RH levels at which the death rates of dried cells not only increased rapidly but displayed a bilinear nature at 50 per cent RH and a high mutant rate at 40 per cent RH, also, it has been known for a long time that the RH at which x-ray diffraction studies of DNA or protein are made affects the results obtained. In more recent times, the correct relationship between one DNA helix and another has been suggested as being controlled by cross linking histones which, on drying, shrink considerably and may become dissociated from the DNA (Richards, 1964). It would seem not unreasonable to assume that water molecules common to both the DNA and histone type proteins exist which form part of the structure of the individual macromolecules and also conjugate the two moieties. Their removal, therefore, could destroy not only the biological integrity of the conjugated macromolecule, but also that of its individual components.

Histones as such have not been described in bacteria but in some of our more recent work we have isolated what appears to be a lysine rich histone strongly attached to the lipid fraction of disrupted *Staphylococcus albus*. The molecule has all the characteristics of a histone in that it is rich in lysine, partly dialysable having a molecular weight of around 40,000 and moreover, its infra-red spectrum is identical to that of other histones. The

TABLE 3-VIII
THE AMINO ACID ANALYSIS OF A BASIC PROTEIN* ISOLATED FROM THE LIPID FRACTION
OF *Staphylococcus epidermides*

| Amino Acid | $\mu$ moles x $10^2$ | Approximate Molecular Ratio with Alanine as 1 |
|---|---|---|
| Alanine | 3.0 | 1 |
| Aspartic | 11.8 | 4 |
| Arginine | — | — |
| Cysteine | — | — |
| Glutamic | 8.6 | 3 |
| Glycine | 12.3 | 4 |
| Histidine | — | — |
| Leusine | 12.2 | 4 |
| Isolecine | 29.4 | 10 |
| Lysine | 38.0 | 13 |
| Methionine | — | — |
| $NH_3$ | 26.0 | — |
| Phenylalanine | 15.6 | 3 |
| Proline | — | — |
| Serine | 5.5 | 2 |
| Threonine | — | — |
| Tyrosine | — | — |
| Valine | 24.4 | 8 |

*This protein was extracted with the lipid fraction of cells and could not be separated from the lipids by solvents or column chromatography.

aminoacid composition of this compound is shown in Table 3-VIII and its infra-red spectrum in Fig. 3-11. This histone is firmly attached to one of the main lipid fractions of the staphylococcus for it was not separated by silicic acid column chromatography of the lipids, nor paper chromatography of the silicic acid chromatographic lipid fraction. Partial removal was finally achieved by partial hydrolysis of the lipid with 0.01 HCL (Bergh, Webb and McArthur, in print). The above is part of the Ph.D. program of Mr. A. K. Bergh on the lipids and stability of microbial cells and it is interesting to note that no such bound histone was found with any of the lipids of organisms sensitive to desiccation such as *E. coli* or *Serratia marcescens*. The rate at which histone synthesis occurs and its relationship to DNA replication in plant and animal cells shows a remarkable resemblance to the rate at which the "early proteins" or phase one protein synthesis took place in our investigations. For instance, in the nuclei of tobacco cells, protein bound to DNA are produced rapidly in the first ten to fifteen minutes whereas proteins bound to RNA do

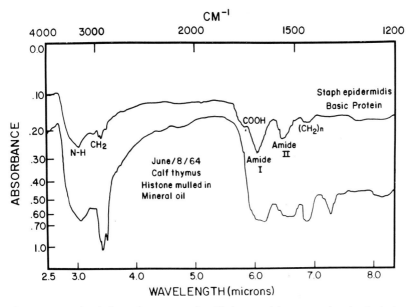

Figure 3-11  The infra-red spectra of calf thymus histone and a basic lysine
rich protein isolated from the lipids of *Staph. epidermides.*

not appear for about twenty minutes (Flamm and Birnstiel. 1964).
In addition, it has been suggested by Umana *et al.* that in liver
cells the DNA-histone ratio must attain a certain level before the
synthesis of DNA can begin. Such findings viewed together with
our own experimental results which suggested that a given
amount of early protein was necessary before bacterial DNA replication took place, and possibly phage DNA also, make it hard
to believe these correlations are chance phenomena. Their similarity to one another can hardly be a coincidence. We strongly believe, therefore, that the synthesis of this "early protein" is required by all cells but we consider it to have a much greater
physical role than its physiological one. These beliefs were
strengthened by our subsequent work and in Chapter 6, an attempt is made to correlate our findings and those of other workers
into the role of bound water and "early proteins" not only with
regards to cell and gene stability, but also to protein and nucleic
acid synthesis. On the point of cell stability towards desiccation,

however, it is pertinent to note at this point that in stable cells such as *Staphylococcus albus* or Mycobacteria inositol is a known natural structural ingredient of many macromolecules, including the nucleoproteins, moreover, some unidentified cyclic amino-phenolic type of compounds have been recently found in fractions of our *Staphylococcus*.

Our investigations so far had shown desiccation to be muta-genic and hence DNA damage appeared to occur. As to whether or not this was due to a direct action of drying on the DNA or to the stresses imposed upon it by the shrinkage of associated pro-teins needed some thought. Considered logically phage DNA was more stable after the synthesis of "early protein" but only while in the cell. Also, if stable cells do have histone-like protein it would appear that to some extent this protein actually stabilizes the DNA. Moreover, since inositol could prevent virus inactivation, inside or outside a cell, we concluded that there is a direct effect of bound water loss on the biological integrity of DNA. It is just possible, in the light of our lipid investigations, that in a stable cell the "histone" is bound to the DNA partly by hydrophobic lipids, whereas in unstable ones this is accomplished by water alone. If there is a direct effect of bound water loss on DNA then is becomes necessary to explain why back mutations are prevented by metabolites and why cells grown on minimal medium and de-siccated in the spent medium as a "slurry" are so stable from both the genetic and viability standpoints. We could only assume that the metabolically produced small molecules actually affix them-selves to the DNA of the cell and form part of the biologically active genes.

Throughout this work on the physiology of desiccation, our attention was drawn repeatedly to another similarity between our work and that being conducted in the field of radiation biology. Desiccation could do all those things attributed, at that time, to be unique effects of ultraviolet light or x-rays. We had produced mutations, released latent lambda phage, effected the virus "capac-ity" of cells in the same way as do radiations and found phage stability inside the host cell to follow the same time sequences as it does when irradiated. It seemed pertinent, therefore, to look into the relationships between bound water and radiation damage. By carrying out such investigations, we hoped to learn something of the mechanism of radiation damage and the way in which compounds such as inositol were able to protect cells.

# CHAPTER 4

# THE INTERACTION BETWEEN RADIATIONS, CHEMICALS AND BOUND WATER

## The Influence of the Bound Water Content of Cells on Ultraviolet and Visible Light Damage

MUCH OF THE WORK on the action of light on bacterial cells has been conducted with suspensions of cells in water or films on the surface of agar. Although there has been extensive work on the effects of environment on bacterial aerosols in the dark (Chapter 1), little has been reported on the behaviour of air-borne cells exposed to ultraviolet (UV) and visible light. The work reported on this topic has been reviewed by Wells (1955) who found most of the investigations had concerned themselves with the ability of light of wavelengths between 2500A and 2800A to destroy cells with complete disregard to any effect of the relative humidity (RH) at which the experiments were conducted. However, Wells and Wells (1936) and Koller (1939 and 1952), in studying radiation effects, were able to demonstrate that air-borne cells were more resistant to UV radiations when suspended in air of a high RH than in air of a low RH, and also that air-borne cells at any RH were far more sensitive to UV than cells in suspension in water or buffer solution.

To ascertain the mechanism by which UV destroys cells, many workers have attempted to correlate the absorption band of cell components with the relative lethality of various wavelengths and since UV of around 2600A appeared to be the most lethal, the nucleic acids were considered as the absorbing and damaged components. Early studies on the kinetics of radiation deaths indicated that several processes were involved (Zelle, 1955), but as to the exact cause of death, some workers believed it to be due to the production of substances such as hydrogen peroxide poisonous to the cell, others like Lea and co-workers (1936) maintained that the kinetics and temperature coefficients characteristic of death by irradiation did not conform to those of death by disinfection and suggested death due to UV light was probably the result of the rupture of a vital molecule. Similarly, workers studying the photo-reactivation of irradiated cells have assumed that death results from the production of a toxin by one wavelength and its destruction by another, or alternatively, that reactivation does not affect the UV damage but avoids its consequences by initiating the synthesis of a substance acting as an alternative metabolite. Both theories required the participation of a photochemical synthesis which either blocks or frees a particular metabolic pathway.

In the past few years, we have become accustomed to more sophisticated experiments with monochromatic light such as the studies of Zelle and Hollaender (1956) and the introduction of action spectra and quantum yields, as well as the renowned target theory. Works of this kind and published papers on the topic are far too numerous to be indexed in a monograph but it is perhaps pertinent to note that experiments of this kind were carried out by Gates, as far back as 1929, who reported 2652 A light to be the most lethal wavelength. Basically, because with bacteria and some viruses the action spectrum of inactivation resembles the absorption spectrum of nucleic acids, it is assumed that the DNA or RNA is the target of the radiation. As a consequence of this, other workers (Beukers and Berends, 1960) have isolated radiation products of thymine and the thymine dimer has become considered to be the main reason for cell death and perhaps mutation (Wacker, 1963). However, along with these dimers, water addition products as well as many other unidentified mixed dimers, occur. The former photoproduct is usually dismissed because it is said to be unstable to heating, but unfortunately, it is often not realized that a virus or a bacterial cell does not particularly like being heated either and from a biological point of view the water addition product may be extremely important. Moreover, a correlation between the amount of dimers found and the number of deaths does not prove the dimer to be the cause of death; it could very well be a consequence of death. The argument that the nucleic acid is the target of radiations because of action spectra correlations is fair only if a cell is unaffected by radiations absorbed by other molecules. However, this is not the case, since both bacteria and viruses are inactivated by wavelengths longer than 3000 A. Under these latter circumstances, the question arises as to whether the death mechanism is different or whether the absorbed energy migrates to the nucleic acids. The exact point of maximum efficiency of UV light varies with different organisms (Wagner and Mitchell, 1955) and, in addition, there are numerous investigations showing that energy absorbed by one molecule can migrate within and between macrocolecules (Shore and Pardee, 1956; Setlow, 1957; Arnoff, 1957). That the same bond may be broken by the absorption of different wavelengths of light such as 2800 A and 5400 A, and energy migrations of up to 100 A can occur, has been demonstrated by the work of Frank and Livingstone (1949). The action spectra experiments, therefore, are perhaps necessary but certainly not sufficient to argue cause of death. Using the same line of thought to suggest the radiation-produced dimers cause death necessitates the demonstration that cells cannot be killed by light unless dimers are formed, and this does not appear to have been considered. The target theory also appears in many respects as a mathematical mystery for although it seems to hold with dried organisms, with wet or partially dried cells multiplicity changes occur and hit numbers ranging from two to twenty have been recorded (Setlow and Pollard, 1962). Hit numbers of two have been described as meaning the nucleus of a bacterium to be diploid, or having two nuclei or two genes controlling the same metabolic function, but microbiologically there appears to be no such thing as a bacterial nucleus. The same applies to yeasts where several workers have interpreted a multi-hit curve as due to their diploid strain in which a nucleus, let alone the number of chromosomes, is in doubt. In addition, calculated "sensitive" volumes appear to range from a whole virus particle to a couple of nucleotide pairs and become bigger or smaller with dose rate or temperature. As pointed out by Hotz and Zimmer, (1963) calculations of target volumes are open to question

and do not necessarily lead to meaningful results. This is undoubtedly due to the fact that very few workers have paid attention to the influence of the growth medium, stage of growth, and the environmental conditions under which the experiments were conducted. For many years now, it has been known to biologists that these factors alter the shape and slope of log death or mutation versus dose curves. Moreover, dose rate has appeared equally important in the type of result obtained with low doses. The target theory has perhaps been successful in accounting for some quantitative effects of radiations on mutations and inactivations of microorganisms and does describe, in part, the biological effects of high energy radiations on dried material. However, the living cell is not dry and it is particularly disappointing to realize that very few workers have attempted to correlate their findings with the *life* of a cell; in other words, to use radiations as a means of studying the life processes rather than those of death.

The damage caused by radiations has proven difficult to analyze partly because little information exists about the physicochemical changes induced in cells by low dose ranges. We felt, therefore, that a study of the action of various radiations with respect to the water content of cells might help to disentangle at least one effect from the many others.

In our first series of studies, we utilized the aerosol drum fitted with the transparent plastic and irradiated from outside with germicidal lamps each generating 0.22 w. of 2800-3200 A light or G.E.R.S. sunlamps with a complete spectrum from 2800 to 7500 A. These lamps generate 1.7 w. in the 2800 to 3200 A Region and 7.0 w. in the 4000 to 6000 A band. To separate various wavebands filters were made using solutions of dyes held between two nine-inch square plastic plates. These filters had a light path of 0.25 inches. In later experiments, we used plastic filters manufactured by dissolving the plastic and dye in chloroform and then evaporating off the solvent. Since the drum and the air within it rotate, the suspended cells statistically receive the same dose, but the exact measurement of this proved initially to be an almost impossible task. However, as the main object of our work was to compare the effects of dose with water content, lamp distance from the drum and irradiation time became our criteria of dose measurement. This technique has been utilized by many other work-ers where exact dose measurements are difficult or irrelevant to the comparative type of study undertaken. As a result of our find-ings from these experimentations, a second drum with fitted in-ternal lamps was built and used to determine whether some of the effects noted could be demonstrated with the shorter wavelengths utilized by most workers. With this drum, a more accurate mea-surement of dose could be made, so dose rather than time was used in the analysis of results, and dose-rate as well as dose versus RH could be studied.

First, we examined the effect of various wavebands over a thirty-minute period of continuous irradiation, utilizing a rela-tive humidity of 30 per cent, inositol, and lamp distance of twelve inches. The results demonstrated that light of up to 5800 A was able to destroy cells although the shape of the log survival versus time curves changed from an apparent exponential type with the 2800-3200 A band to a sigmoidal (or multihit type) with the longer wavelengths. The shoulder of the curve or lag phase during which no deaths occurred lengthened as the wavelength increased (Fig. 4-I). If cells stained with a photodynamic dye were irradiated, their sensitivity to visible light increased but this sensitization was found to be due primarily to a decrease in the duration of the lag period, rather than the slope of the subsequent death rate curve. From Fig. 4-I, it appeared that even with the 2800-3200 A light a slight shoulder to the curve existed. Since the G.E.R.S. lamp emitted 1.7 w. of 2800-3200 A light while the germicidal lamp only emitted 0.22 w., we next examined the effect of in-creasing the intensity by utilizing batteries of up to eight lamps but were unable to reach the same death rate as that produced by the R.S. sunlamp alone (Webb, 1961a). From this, we con-cluded that if given simultaneously, the lethal action of the vari-ous wavelengths were additive. To substantiate the argument we used, first, mixtures of light given simultaneously and second, a ten-minute exposure to 2800-3200 A light was followed immedi-ately by irradiation with 3400-4500 A or 5200-5800 A light. The first set of experiments showed clearly that the effects were addi-tive but surprisingly when UV irradiated cells were exposed im-mediately to light of 3400-4500 A more viable cells were recovered

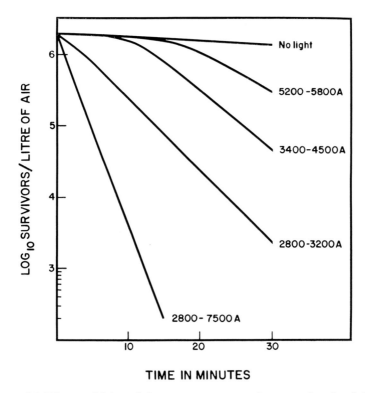

**TIME IN MINUTES**

Figure 4-1 The sensitivity of *S. marcescens* to various wavebands of light when irradiated for thirty minutes in aerosols held at 30 per cent RH (Taken from Webb, *Canad. J. Microbiol., 7,* 1961a).

than were obtained without the second irradiation. In addition, the subsequent death rate on continuous irradiation with the visible light was the same as that produced by these wavelengths alone, but no shoulder to the curve was apparent. These results suggested very strongly that the phenomenon of photo-reactivation was operative in aerosols and that the reactivation was extremely rapid, indicating a physical rather than a physiological reason. Moreover, the addition of a photodynamic dye not only increased the sensitivity of the cells to visible light but also increased the percentage of cells "reactivated" (Webb, 1961a).

These preliminary experiments gave us an idea as to the magnitude of radiation damage we could expect in an aerosol. It was evident that visible light was lethal to the cells provided the exposure time was sufficiently long. The work agreed in part with that of Kaplan (1952) and others who have found stained cells and viruses more sensitive to visible radiations. However, the action of the dye appeared to be connected not only with its absorption spectrum but also with its fluorescence or method of dissipating absorbed energy, for in every case, red dyes acted as desensitizing agents. Moreover, insoluble dyes had no action whatsoever, demonstrating the necessity of the dye to enter the cell and combine with molecules inside the cell in order to exercise its function rather than form an association with the outside of the cell wall. We were a little disappointed by the magnitude of the death rate since in each experiment we had added inositol to stabilize the cells against "dark" death and it looked very much as though inositol offered little or no protection to irradiated cells. Certainly we found the sensitivity of air-borne cells to be much greater than cells in suspensions or even in films on the surface of agar plates, confirming the observations of Wells (1936). Although it has been repeatedly stated that dose rate plays no role in the type of dose response inactivation curves obtained with a given organism, we nevertheless decided to examine the effect of lower intensities over a fifteen-minute R.S. sunlamp or thirty-minute germicidal lamp exposure time with and without inositol. This seemed a reasonable thing to do, since the number of deaths occurring in thirty-minutes in the dark was negligible in comparison to that produced by the light. However, in order to overcome any criticism on this point, we decided to present our data as a ratio of the number of survivors in the dark $(N_D)$ over the number of irradiated survivors $(N_R)$. The results shown in Fig. 4-2 show that an approximate ten-fold drop in dose with the R.S. sunlamp or germicidals resulted in a ten-fold increase in the number of survivors when inositol was absent. Such a finding indicated that the number of deaths was directly proportioned to the dose. However, with inositol such was not the case. A ten-fold decrease in the dose delivered by the R.S. sunlamp resulted in almost a 1000-fold increase in survivors as did a four-fold decrease in that delivered by the germicidal lamp. Estimates of the average dose rate of 2800-3200 A light indicated that approximately 50 ergs/-

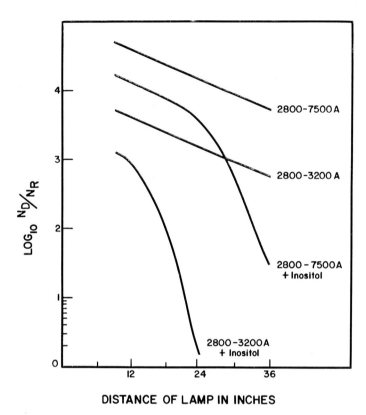

Figure 4-2  The action of inositol and the influence of intensity on the sensitivity of *S. marcescens* to 2800-3200A light and 2800-7500A light when the cells are held in aerosols at 30 per cent RH. $N_D$ = number of survivors in dark aerosols. $N_R$ = number of survivors in irradiated aerosols (taken from Webb, *J. Appl. Bacteriol., 26*, 1963b).

$cm^2$/sec. were delivered into the drum when the R.S. lamp was placed four feet away. With the germicidals at two feet, the dose rate was about 25 ergs/$cm^2$/sec. From these experiments, it was evident that cell protection by inositol was small at high dose rates of light but that its ability to prevent damage increased rapidly with decreasing intensity. From our previous work, it was logical to conclude that at these low dose rates a marked effect of relative humidity ought to be found. To test our hypothesis we conducted a series of experiments at various RH levels, utilizing the germicidal lamps at twenty-four inches and the R.S. lamps at four feet from the drum. A thirty-minute exposure time was employed for the former and fifteen minutes for the latter.

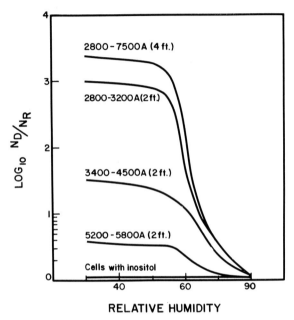

**RELATIVE HUMIDITY**

Figure 4-3 The effect of RH and inositol on the sensitivity of air-borne cells of *S. marcescens* toward various wavebands of light. The lamp distances, shown in brackets, are those found to give maximal RH effects (taken from Webb, *J. Appl. Bacteriol., 26,* 1963b).

It was gratifying to discover a pronounced and sharp effect of RH. At 80 per cent RH few deaths occurred with either type of lamp, but as the RH fell between 70 and 55 per cent a rapid increase in the radiation sensitivity of the cells was observed (Fig. 4-3); moreover, inositol completely prevented damage at the low humidities. Thus, it appeared that the same critical RH range observed earlier with desiccation alone existed as far as radiation damage was concerned. Since light of up to 5800A had been shown to be lethal to air-borne cells, it seemed reasonable to expect that if the kind of cell damage differed in accordance with the wavelength of light, then the effect of RH should also differ.

This hypothesis was tested using the filtered RS sunlamp radiation with the lamp twenty-four inches from the drum. However, although the absolute number of cell deaths per thirty-minute time period decreased as the wavelength increased, 55-70 per cent RH was always the critical level at which abrupt changes occurred (Fig. 4-3, Webb, 1963b). Equally significant, however, was the change in the shape of the "decay" curve as the humidity increased. At RH values below 50 per cent, exponential rates were obtained with 2800-3200A light, whereas above this level the plots log recovery versus time always displayed a shoulder which became longer as the humidity increased (Fig. 4-4). These results simulated the findings of Morowitz (1953) where the irradiation of dry spores of *B. subtilis* obeyed the reciprocity law whereas wet spores did not, and as pointed out by Setlow and Pollard (1962),

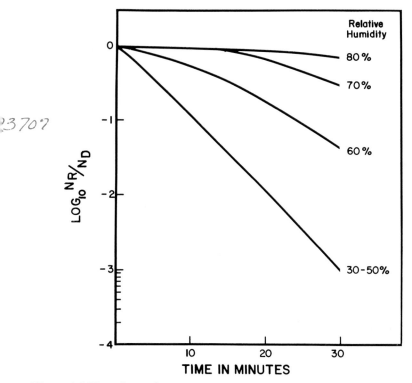

Figure 4-4 The effects of RH on the survival of air-borne *S. marcescens* when irradiated with 2800-3200A light at a dose rate of 25 ergs./cm²/sec.

any straight-forward physical interpretation of the wet spore data in terms of multiplicities is open to question.

Following the same lines as our experiments with dark aerosols, we began to look for any influence RH might have on the incidence of mutations in the surviving cells and the ability of irradiated cells to be infected by and synthesize bacteriophages. During the first series of experiments with *Serratia marcescens,* outlined above, we had scored the number of white mutants and were surprised to find an extremely high incidence of the white cell mutants between 40 and 50 per cent RH. In some cases, the number reached some 10,000 per $10^6$ survivors, in other words, one in a hundred survivors were mutants. This, of course, far exceeded any other type of mutant frequency and naturally the results were open to serious criticism. However, the sensitivity of these white cells to the light was no different from the parent red variety so selection due to differential resistance was not operative. Some strains of *S. marcescens,* especially in aging cultures, are known to produce as many as 50 per cent white variants, so we considered that pigment deficiency might not be a good indication of mutation. Therefore, we turned our attention to the lactose positive (Lac+) to lactose negative (Lac−) mutation, as well as amino acid deficiencies. In the former case, lactose EMB-Agar was used and in the latter, the irradiated cells were incubated for one hour in amino acids, washed in saline and plated on minimal medium (M.M.), allowed to grow for eighteen hours and then an overlay of amino acid agar was applied. After a further eighteen-hour incubation period, the newly developing colonies were scored. Some of these colonies were isolated, grown in a full medium, washed and plated onto M.M. to check whether or not a true deficiency existed. The result shown in Fig. 4-5 demonstrated once again that the highest number of mutants was obtained at about 40 per cent RH, and in addition, inositol or high RH completely prevented their occurrence, Webb, (1964). The same was found to be true when back mutants of arginine, thymine, methionine and tryptophan requiring cells were studied as well as the streptomycin dependent to independent back mutation (Fig. 4-5). More significant, when cells were aerosolised in the presence of the required metabolite or lactose, few mutants were obtained simulating the results found with desiccation alone. Moreover, cells grown in M.M. plus the required metabolite and aerosolized as a slurry also displayed a reduced incidence of mutations. It was clear, therefore, that under the conditions described, mutations due to irradiation were dependent on the bound water content of the cell. The odd point was that the maximal number of mutants occurred at 40 per cent RH or at a cell water content of about 10 gms./100 gms. of cell solids and not at the very low water content levels. This implied that the remaining water molecules played some role in the production of mutant cells, suggesting their re-orientation rather than their removal was essential to the mutagenic process.

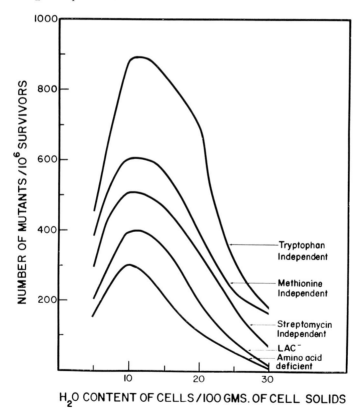

Figure 4-5 The effect of the bound water content of air-borne *E. coli* cells on the production of various mutants by 2800-3200A ultraviolet light delivered at a dose rate of 25 ergs./cm²/sec. Total dose 1.5x10⁴ergs./cm².

The number of mutant cells obtained appeared to be much higher than that obtained by the irradiation of liquid suspensions of cells with germicidal lamps. Several workers have reported back mutant numbers of cells reaching about $10^3$ per $10^7$ survivors and on occasions numbers of 300-500 per $10^6$ survivors have been found. The aerosolised cells appear to produce from five to ten times as many and with relatively low doses of 2800-3200 A light. This was thought to be due to the same phenomenon which results in the extreme sensitivity of air-borne cells to UV or visible light as compared to cells in suspension. In fact, under the experimental conditions described, the finding that no mutants appeared at 80 per cent RH or over was a strong indication that this light intensity or wavelength would not induce mutations in cells irradiated in suspensions. We naturally checked this point and found it to be true, but during the course of this investigation, another phenomenon was noted with our Lac+ cells. Under irradiation from black light (3000-4000 A), these cells could not manufacture $\beta$-galactosidase although the cells remained viable.

As we had found with simple desiccation, the "capacity" of *E. coli B* to support T2 virus was little affected by the radiations so there was no point in examining the effects of inositol. With T3 and T7 coliphages, however, there was a pronounced effect. At relative humidities above 65 per cent the "capacity" remained intact but below 65 per cent the sensitivity increased sharply with decreasing RH and maximal destruction occurred at 45 per cent RH (Fig. 4-6). In addition, the vegatative phage of T2 infected cells showed the same pattern of sensitivity provided the cells were irradiated within ten to twelve minutes after infection. No effect of the light could be found if the irradiation was carried out at longer post-infection times (Fig. 4-7). It was noted also that the RH range at which T2 vegetative phage inactivation occurred shifted towards lower humidities as the post-infection time increased and a possible reason for this phenomenon would have escaped us had it not been for the very astute observation by my technician, Mr. Norman Jackson, that "black" light inhibited $\beta$-galactosidase synthesis, Webb (1963c).

Bearing in mind the two-phased protein and RNA synthesis we had observed earlier, we naturally wondered whether a lethal

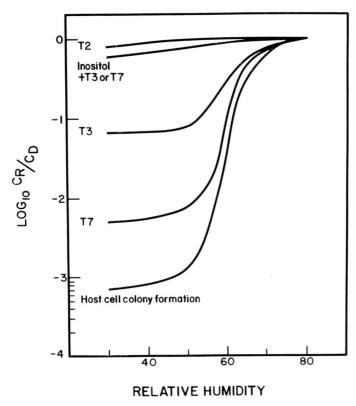

RELATIVE HUMIDITY

Figure 4-6 The effect of RH and inositol on the capacity of *E. coli* B to manufacture T2, T3 and T7 coliphages after being irradiated with 4.5x10⁴ ergs./cm² of 2800-3200A ultraviolet light. $C_R$ = capacity of irradiated airborne cells. $C_D$ = capacity of non-irradiated air-borne cells.

dose of UV irradiation would stop enzyme synthesis and whether the same sequence of events observed with the vegetative T2, T3 and T7 radiation sensitivity with respect to incubation time prior to irradiation would be operative for an adaptive enzyme. We were gratefully rewarded when experiments demonstrated quite clearly that a dose of 2800-3200 A light which killed 99 per cent of the cells only destroyed the cells' ability to produce β- galactosidase if they were irradiated within fifteen to twenty minutes after exposure to the sugar (Fig. 4-8). Obviously, the phenomenon of early protein synthesis in stabilizing the vegetative phages and the

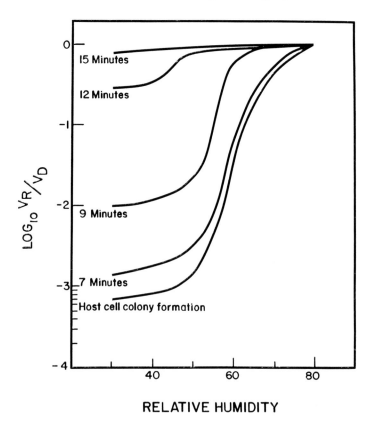

**RELATIVE HUMIDITY**

Figure 4-7 The effect of RH and post infection time prior to drying on the sensitivity of T2 vegetative phage in infected cells of *E. coli B* to 4.5x104 ergs./cm² of 2800-3200A ultraviolet light. $V_R$ = number of vegetative phages surviving the radiation. $V_D$ = number of vegetative phages surviving in the dark.

ability to manufacture β- galactosidase were somehow related. To try to elucidate this problem we followed the uptake of $C^{14}$ uracil and $C^{14}$ thymine in cells continuously irradiated for forty-five minutes with 3000-4000 A light. The intensity used was adjusted to produce a minimal number of deaths ranging from 5 per cent to 10 per cent with 3000-4000 A light. The cells were washed, starved for sixty minutes in phosphate buffer and then transferred to 10.0 ml. of media (described in Chapter Three) and placed under a G.E. Bl "Black Light" fluorescent lamp. Samples were taken at zero, five, ten, fifteen, thirty and forty-five minutes, placed in 10.0 ml. of 0.5 per cent TCA, immediately deposited on a millipore filter and washed by passing 20 ml. of water through the filter. Radioactive (RA) counts were then determined.

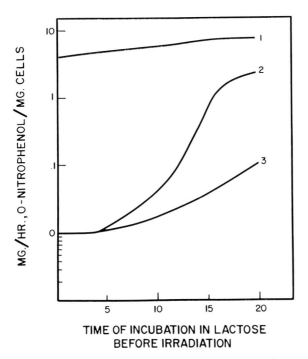

TIME OF INCUBATION IN LACTOSE
BEFORE IRRADIATION

Figure 4-8 The effect of incubation time in lactose prior to drying at 30 per cent RH and irradiation with 3.0x10⁴ ergs./cm² of 2800-3200A ultraviolet light. After incubation the cells were deposited on millipore filters, dried and irradiated then incubated for sixty minutes in lactose-aminoacid medium and sonically disrupted. 1 = β-galactosidase activity in lysates of non-irradiated control cells. 2 = β-galactosidase activity in lysates of irradiated cells. 3 = β-galactosidase activity in lysates of cells prior to irradiation. Total incubation time in lactose of 1 and 2 = 60 minutes plus the pre-incubation time.

The results were remarkable in that, while uracil uptake was only slightly inhibited by the light, the incorporation of amino acids during the first twenty minutes was slowed considerably and thymine uptake was almost completely suppressed. We felt that the use of this non-lethal light should provide us with a new method of examining the relationship between DNA, RNA and protein synthesis as a function of time. Starved cells of *E. coli* were pre-incubated for periods of five to twenty minutes in amino acids (0.3 per cent) plus glucose (1.0 per cent) and then irradiated continuously for forty-five minutes with "Black" light. No effect of the light was found after a fifteen minute period of pre-incubation, thymine and amino acid uptakes were normal. In later experiments, glucose was omitted from the pre-incubation medium but the results were the same, suggesting that the active components of the medium were the amino acids. Knowing that the light would inhibit β- galactosidase synthesis, we next examined the synthesis of this enzyme with respect to pre-incubation time both in amino acids alone and in amino acids with lactose (1 per cent). Pre-incubation in amino acids alone, however, did not prevent the light from inhibiting the synthesis of the enzyme, but if the cells were incubated in lactose plus aminoacids for fifteen to twenty minutes prior to irradiation, the light completely failed to stop the manufacture of the enzyme. Under these circumstances, lactose appeared to be the active ingredient of the pre-incubation medium. This raised the important question as to why a cell, apparently functioning normally, could not produce an adaptive enzyme under continuous irradiation unless pre-incubated in the dark for fifteen minutes with the inducer molecule. In later experiments, we examined the ability of *E. coli B* to manufacture T2, T3 and T7 bacteriophages and in every case the same fifteen minute to twenty minute dark incubation period in aminoacids prevented any action of the light. With the infected cells, pre-incubated or not, uracil incorporation was extremely small, indicating that the light did not prevent the virus from stopping host RNA synthesis, hence phage adsorption and penetration of viral DNA into the cell must have taken place. In order to simplify the presentation of these results, Table 4-I was compiled to demonstrate the generality of the fifteen- to twenty-minute pre-incubation time required for adaptive enzyme synthesis, bacteriophage and DNA replication. All these phenomenon seem to rely on early protein synthesis or the association of an inducer molecule with host DNA, and it would seem more than a coincidence that these same pre-incubation times are precisely those needed to afford the vegetative phages maximum stability towards either desiccation or lethal UV light.

TABLE 4-I

THE ACTION OF 3000-4000 A LIGHT ON VARIOUS METABOLIC ACTIVITIES OF *E. coli*. WITH RESPECT TO INCUBATION TIME BEFORE IRRADIATION

| Metabolic Activity | | Incubation Time Prior to Irradiation | | | | |
|---|---|---|---|---|---|---|
| | | 0 | 5 | 10 | 15 | 20 |
| Thymine uptake | A | (402) nil | 54 | 189 | 398 | 385 |
| | B | (1047) 206 | 251 | 752 | 1093 | 1042 |
| Uracil Uptake | A | (621) 589 | 686 | 721 | 699 | 732 |
| | B | (1700) 1684 | 1746 | 1698 | 1751 | 1721 |
| Aminoacid Uptake | A | (374) 82 | (420) 210 | (618) 504 | (956) 1053 | (1299) 3146 |
| | B | (1821) 702 | (2025) 894 | (2253) 1846 | (2484) 2719 | (2768) 3146 |
| β- galactosidase Synthesis. | | (2.1) nil | 0.1 | 1.8 | (4.2) 4.3 | (4.7) 4.8 |
| Phage T1. | | | 9 | 27 | 68 | 83 | 86 |
| Phage T2. | | | 18 | 32 | 71 | 103 | 94 |
| Phage T3 | | | 16 | 29 | 72 | 85 | 83 |
| Phage T7 | | | 14 | 31 | 75 | 81 | 85 |

A = Radioactive count/$10^7$ cells after fifteen minutes irradiation.
B = Radioactive count/$10^7$ cells after forty-five minutes irradiation.
1. Figures in brackets represent the RA count of controls at an equivalent total incubation time. With thymine and uracil this represents fifteen or forty-five minutes irradiation time only because the base was added after the pre-incubation time. With the amino acids the figures in brackets = fifteen or forty-five minutes irradiation time plus the pre-incubation time because each of the added amino acids were labelled.
2. β-galactosidase activity expressed in mg./ml. of o-nitrophenol/mg. cells in sonic lysate after forty-five minutes irradiation in lactose amino acid medium.
3. Phage results expressed as a percentage of the viruses obtained the controls over the same total incubation time. Phage to bacterial cells ratio 2:1.
4. Dose rate 120 ergs./cm²/sec. Total Dose = 3.2x10⁵ ergs./cm².

In order to examine these phenomena more carefully, we repeated the above experiments, using a minimal medium instead of the aminoacid medium. To the M.M. we added the $C^{14}$ metabolite under study. Next, we examined the incorporation of arginine and methionine, using an arginine and a methionine dependent strain of *E. coli* respectively. For the former, Difco arginine assay medium was used and for the latter a full medium less methionine was prepared in our laboratories. With the thymine requiring mutant in minimal medium a smaller effect of light on thymine uptake was found during the first twenty minutes, however, following this period incorporation was considerably slower than the controls. We could only surmise that the light prevented the synthesis either of amino acids or of proteins essential for further DNA replication and that the attachment of amino acid precursors to the DNA allowed the latter to partly replicate. This latter assumption was rendered more plausible first by the demonstration that pre-incubation in amino acids prior to irradiation allowed the cell to behave normally under irradiation, and second, by the effect of the light on the incorporation of individual amino acids. It is well known that if the end product of a metabolic chain is supplied to a bacterial cell, the intermediate metabolites are not manufactured nor are the required enzymes. This is especially true for amino acids. The results of such experiments with *E. coli* B or the mutant cells in minimal medium plus a single $C^{14}$ labelled L-amino acid of high specific activity indicated that only the incorporation of certain amino acids were affected by the light. Arginine, lysine, alanine, leucine, serine and proline uptakes were all inhibited while those of glutamic, phenylalanine, tyrosine and methionine were not (Table 4-II). Moreover, pre-incubation of the cells for fifteen minutes with the particular amino acid completely prevented the action of light (Webb and Singh Bhorjee, 1964).

The very high level of arginine uptake compared with any of the other amino acids strongly suggested that the formation of basic or histone-like proteins occurred during the first fifteen minutes. Moreover, the synthesis of these proteins appeared necessary for DNA replication. The latter seemed a logical conclusion, first because the uptake of thymine did not occur until they were formed and second because the "black" light reduced the uptake of arginine by 75 per cent and partially inhibited the incorporation of only those amino acids normally found in basic proteins. When we repeated these experiments with *Staph. epidermidis*, we found the uptake of all those amino acids present in the isolated basic protein mentioned in Chapter 3 to be inhibited by the "black" light and moreover, attempts to obtain this protein from irradiated cells failed. However, failure could not be considered

TABLE 4-II
THE EFFECT OF 3000-4000 Å LIGHT ON THE UPTAKE OF THYMINE
URACIL AND AMINO ACIDS BY *E. coli.* IN MINIMAL MEDIUM PLUS
THE METABOLITE WITH RESPECT TO PRE-INCUBATION TIME

| Metabolite | | Incubation Time before Irradiation | | | |
|---|---|---|---|---|---|
| | | 0 | 5 | 10 | 15 |
| Thymine | A | 372 | — | — | — |
| | B | 34 | 46 | 168 | 383 |
| Uracil | A | 705 | — | — | — |
| | B | 662 | 664 | 643 | 688 |
| Arginine | A | 4331 | 8436 | 13943 | 18429 |
| | B | 1005 | 2158 | 13745 | 19270 |
| Lysine | A | 1477 | 2077 | 2477 | 2955 |
| | B | 1084 | 1250 | 2366 | 2834 |
| Glutamic | A | 2996 | 3244 | 3729 | 4295 |
| | B | 3212 | 3419 | 3684 | 4384 |
| Methionine | A | 1285 | 1496 | 1760 | 2152 |
| | B | 1397 | 1502 | 1784 | 2549 |
| Alanine | A | 1021 | 1347 | 1538 | 1874 |
| | B | 722 | 819 | 1395 | 2016 |
| Tyrosine | A | 954 | 1103 | 1333 | 1526 |
| | B | 1001 | 1144 | 1306 | 1498 |
| Proline | A | 1042 | 1255 | 1486 | 1664 |
| | B | 798 | 983 | 1242 | 1714 |
| Serine | A | 1122 | 1351 | 1655 | 1814 |
| | B | 813 | 1014 | 1488 | 1846 |
| Phenylalanine | A | 809 | 946 | 1074 | 1206 |
| | B | 852 | 998 | 1107 | 1255 |

Dose rate = 120 ergs. /cm²/sec.
A = RA uptake of the controls over the full incubation period (i.e., dark period plus fifteen minutes for amino acids and fifteen minutes only for thymine and uracil).
B = RA count after fifteen minutes of irradiation plus the pre-incubation time.

too significant, as it was difficult to irradiate uniformly large numbers of cells and the extraction and purification procedure necessary to purify the protein may well have been too elaborate to detect small amounts of the protein. We tried to isolate a similar protein from *E. coli* labelled with $C^{14}$ arginine. To do this, the cells were dried, acetone washed and then extracted with 0.5 N HCl. The HCl extract was adjusted to pH 10 and two volumes of absolute ethanol added. A precipitate was obtained which on electrophoresis proved to be a single protein having a very small positive charge. Hydrolysis of this protein and subsequent chromatography had recently showed it to contain a higher arginine content than the rest of the proteins of the cell. At the present time, work is being conducted with this protein in an effort to analyze it chemically and to ascertain what effect, if any, it has on protein and DNA syntheses. However, regardless of what this work should reveal, it seems that the "early" proteins are basic ones, are necessary for DNA replication, and are responsible for the observed increase in the stability of viral DNA towards desiccation and irradiation some fifteen minutes after infection.

At this time, we had deviated a little from our main lines of research but these findings played an important role in our understanding of the physiological mechanisms of the cell and helped considerably in formulating ideas as to why cells and genes appeared to be more desiccation and radiation resistant if the cells were grown in minimal medium. They also assisted in postulating why incubation in amino acids appears necessary to obtain maximum back mutant yields and so on. These ideas will be discussed in Chapter 6, where an attempt is made at some generalizations from the described works.

Our next series of experiments concerned themselves with the germicidal 2537 A light from lamps fitted inside the drum. Initially, two 12" Slimline G.E. G8T5 lamps, each emitting about 1.3 watts, were used. This treatment proved to be too drastic as a five-second exposure at 80 per cent RH resulted in the survival of only 0.1 per cent of the cells. One of the lamps was removed, but since almost the same drop in viable cell numbers occurred, it became necessary to utilize plastic filters to cut down the intensity of the light from a single lamp. However, with the aid of these filters, the manufacturer's specifications of the lamp and a photo-cell detector, we were able to examine not only the effects of RH but also the influence of dose rate, both as a function of RH and on the protective action of inositol.

As can be seen from Fig. 4-9, the same dose given at different rates at 80 per cent RH did not produce the same number of cell deaths, a phenomenon indicated in Fig. 4-4. In addition, the dose

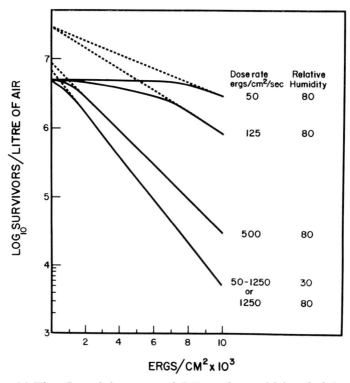

Figure 4-9 The effect of dose-rate and RH on the sensitivity of air-borne *E. coli* to 2537A ultraviolet light.

rate had a pronounced effect on the ability of inositol to protect cells. At 50 ergs./cm²/sec. full protection was afforded the cells at 30 per cent RH up to a total dose of 1x10⁴ergs./cm², whereas at higher dose rates the protection became less. It was apparent, also, that at a dose rate of 500 ergs./cm²/sec., the cells protected with inositol and irradiated at 30 per cent RH displayed the same behaviour as cells irradiated at 80 per cent RH in its absence. Also, the extrapolation of the multi-hit type of curves obtained gave the same "hit" number of about six (Figs. 4-9 and 4-10). This naturally intrigued us and we repeated the experiments with trihydroxycyclohexane, and in each case, provided the dose rate was below 500 ergs./cm²/sec., we obtained a hit value of three (Fig. 4-10). The net result of experiments of this kind led us to conclude that before damage occurred, six water molecules had to be removed or six hydrogen bonds broken between inositol, or water and the UV susceptible macromolecule, or with the hydroxy-cyclohexane since only three protective groups existed all three needed to be affected by the absorption of radiant energy. We carried out many such experiments with different protective chemicals at 30 per cent RH and were quite surprised to find a "hit" number corresponding to the expected one occurred each time.

As a result of these investigations, we turned our attention to other microbes obtaining the same result until we investigated *Staphylococcus albus*. With this organism, some very odd and inconsistent results were obtained. After much work, we discovered

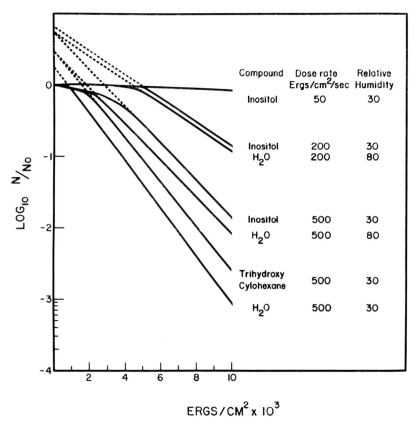

Figure 4-10 The effect of dose-rate, RH and hydroxycyclohexanes on the sensitivity of air-borne *E. coli* to 2537A ultraviolet light.

that the size of the clumps of cells not only determined their susceptibility to drying alone, but also their sensitivity to UV light, and we naturally wondered whether the same phenomenon would apply to non-clumping organisms if more than one cell was placed in each aerosol particle. All through our previous work we had used a spray concentration of approximately $1 \times 10^9$ cells which meant that only one drop in ten generated by the spray contained a cell and so we were sure of monodispersal in our aerosols. It was a relatively simple matter to concentrate the cells by centrifugation and increase the average number of cells per drop from one to twenty. When this was done, the UV sensitivity of the cells decreased and the shape of the curve changed from an exponential type to a sigmoidal or multi-hit type as the number of cells per drop increased, but the hit number did not correspond to the number of cells per particle (Fig. 4-11). These findings simulated those of Wells (1955) with *Sarcina lutea,* who explained an observed delay in disinfection by chemicals and UV to clumping. Such findings, however, cast serious doubts on "hit" numbers obtained in solution with clumping organisms, or for that matter, concentrated suspensions of any cells and make it imperative that if meaningful results are to be obtained from experiments they must be carried out with dilute suspensions of cells, monodispersed aerosols or monolayers of cells on filters or agar surfaces. This was suggested, of course, in Chapter 3, where cells on filters had to be diluted in order to simulate the aerosol death rates on drying, and where inositol was actually found to be toxic to cells if the cell layers were too thick. With ten or more cells per drop RH effects were almost lost. As can be seen from a comparison of Fig. 4-9 and 4-11, the recovery of monodispersed cells at 80 per cent RH and twenty cells/drop at 30 per cent RH only differ by a factor of three after a dose of $1 \times 10^4$ ergs./cm²., whereas with monodispersed cells alone this difference is over 1000. The aerosol is not, therefore, as simple a technique as it appears and considerable experience is needed to understand the things that can seriously affect the results obtained.

Having concluded this series of studies, we reverted to our monodispersed aerosols and examined the effect of RH in modifying the action of 2537A UV on mutant production; enzyme syn-

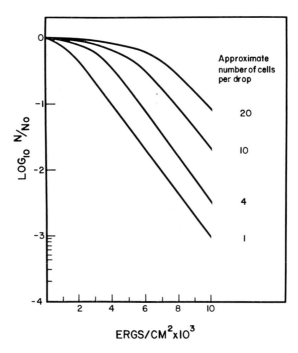

Figure 4-11 The effect of the number of cells per aerosol droplet-nucleus on the death of air-borne *E. coli* cells held at 30 per cent RH and irradiated with 2537A ultraviolet light at 50 ergs./cm²/sec.

thesis; the capacity of *E. coli B* to manufacture coliphages and vegetative phage stability. Two dose rates were used, 50 ergs./-cm²/sec. and 500 ergs./cm²/sec., and it is necessary only to say that all of the phenomena described above with the 2800-3200 A light were observed. The only difference was that the protection afforded these cell functions was less at a dose rate of 500 ergs./-cm²/sec. than at 50 ergs./cm²/sec., as was to be expected, and the dose required to kill an equivalent number of cells at 30 per cent RH with 2537 A light was about one quarter of that required with 2800-3200 A radiation.

Finally, we investigated one more property of the cell - the induction of lysis and the production of Lambda phage by *E. coli K12*. This phenomenon was examined both from the standpoint of bound water content and dose. Under the dose rate conditions described, little or no induction occurred above 75 per cent RH, however, in the absence of inositol a sudden response to the light occurred at 70 per cent RH and a maximal response amounting to about 60 per cent of the cells undergoing lysis was observed at 60 per cent RH. This coincided exactly with the RH range during which an equally sudden decline in the UV sensitivity of other strains of *E. coli* took place. Moreover, to obtain the same degree of lysis, smaller doses were required as the RH was lowered below 60 per cent, suggesting once again that bound water was somehow involved in the attachment of the prophage to host DNA and that prophage inactivation was more easily achieved when bound water was absent (Table 4-III). To check these points, the filter was removed and the effect of a high dose rate from one lamp was examined. As the same doses were required to give maximum lysis, extremely short exposure times at 80 per cent RH were required. At 30 per cent RH little or no lysis was found and this was thought to be due to the impossibly short exposure time required to deliver the correct dosage (Webb and Dumasia, 1964).

TABLE 4-III
THE EFFECT OF RELATIVE HUMIDITY AND 2537 A LIGHT ON THE
LYSIS OF *E. coli K12* AND THE PRODUCTION OF LAMBDA PHAGE

| Dose | | | Relative Humidity | | | |
|---|---|---|---|---|---|---|
| Ergs. X10³ cm² | 30 | 40 | 50 | 60 | 70 | 80 |
| 10 | 5* | 7 | 21 | 62 | 14 | 0.01 |
| 8 | 16 | 21 | 51 | 54 | 4 | 0.002 |
| 5 | 21 | 41 | 44 | 33 | 0.002 | 0.005 |
| 3 | 34 | 15 | 14 | 12 | 0.008 | 0.005 |
| 1 | 12 | 7 | 8 | 6 | 0.006 | 0.004 |

*Results expressed as the percentage of cells undergoing lysis and producing Lambda phage.

## The Effects of Bound Water Content on X-ray Damage to Cells

As has been shown in earlier chapters, cell deaths in aerosols due to UV or desiccation alone do not begin to occur until their water content falls below 30 gms. $H_2O/100$ gms. of cell solids. It was assumed, therefore, that one of the first actions of lethal ultraviolet light was to remove or re-orientate structural water and that this action was mainly responsible for cell death or mutation, even when the cells were treated in aqueous suspensions. The

presence of large amounts of water was considered to be the reason for the larger doses needed to inactivate wet or water suspended cells. To test this idea we decided to examine the effects of
x-rays since this type of radiation is well known to interact with
water.

Cells of *E. coli* B were prepared for aerosolization as previously
described and atomized from water or a 5 per cent solution of
inositol. When the cells aerosolized from water were subjected to

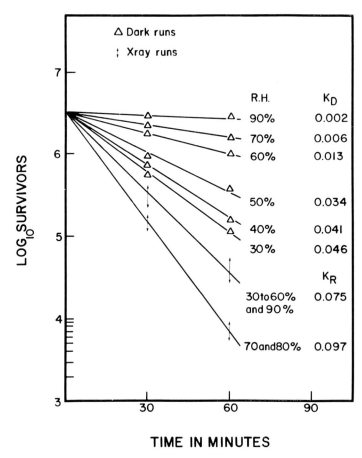

TIME IN MINUTES

Figure 4-12 The effect of RH on the death of air-borne *E. coli* in dark
aerosols and when irradiated for sixty minutes with a 250Kv x-ray machine.
Approximate average dose 15r/minute (taken from Webb and Dumasia,
*Canad. J. Microbiol., 10*, 1964).

continuous irradiation from a 250 kv. x-ray machine for one hour the death rate remained constant at a value of 0.075 between 30 and 60 per cent RH., then increased to 0.097 between 70 and 80 per cent RH and finally decreased to 0.075 at 90 per cent RH (Fig. 4-12). At first sight, this suggested a sharp increase in the sensitivity of the cells to x-rays between 60 and 70 per cent RH, however, it was necessary to view the sensitivity in terms of the rate at which deaths occurred in the absence of the radiation. This kind of data analysis is shown in Fig. 4-13, where the difference between the death rate constant produced by the radiations ($K_R$) and the death rate constant of the desiccated cells in the dark ($K_D$), as well as the bound water content of cells, are plotted against

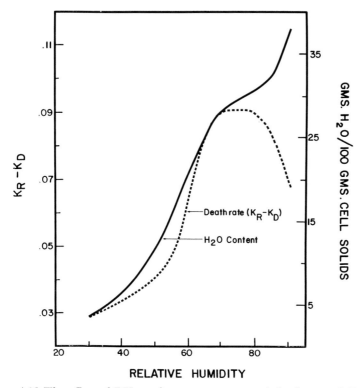

RELATIVE HUMIDITY

Figure 4-13 The effect of RH on the water content and death rate of *E. Coli* produced by x-rays. Irradiation time sixty minutes, approximate dose rate 15r/minute. $K_R$ = death rate on irradiation. $K_D$ = death rate without irradiation (taken from Webb and Dumasia, *Canad. J. Microbiol.*, *10* 1964).

RH. From such an analysis it was clear that the lethal action of x-rays was directly related to the bound water content of the cells and that the maximal rate of increase in x-ray effectiveness as a lethal agent took place when the RH was raised from 60 to 70 per cent. Further, at 90 per cent RH, a point at which multiple water layers start to form, x-ray damage decreased. Since the $K_R$ value remained constant from 30 to 60 per cent RH, it could only be assumed that the major effect of the x-rays was to remove bound water and that most of the deaths resulted from the physical loss of this structural entity from macromolecules. Such an assumption seemed reasonable, first because any direct action of the x-rays on anything other than water should produce a constant increase in $K_R$ values over the $K_D$ values regardless of RH and second, any indirect action of the radiation due to the formation of ions from water also should increase the ratio by a constant amount unless the ionizations took place in strategic parts of the macromolecule. Under the latter circumstances, a distinction between direct and so-called indirect action cannot be made. The fact that the lethality of x-rays decreased at 90 per cent RH and above was taken to mean that multilayers of water were protective and suggested that much of the damage caused by x-ray resulted from its action on structural water rather than free water. It was presumed that the ionization of a free water molecule was non-lethal unless the ions produced were hydrated by a bound water molecule, a phenomenon less likely to occur when large numbers of water molecules were present in the cell.

In the aerosols generated from distilled water, the death rate of cells at 30 per cent RH due to the x-rays ($K_R - K_D$) was 0.029, a relatively high value when compared with the $K_D$ values at any RH level studied. This was thought to be the result of a classical "direct" action of the radiations on the atoms of macromolecules. However, when cells were irradiated in the presence of inositol the cells were not only protected against the RH effect but also against this "direct" action for the difference between $K_R$ and $K_D$ was nil at all levels of RH below 80 per cent. Above 80 per cent RH however, the effectiveness of inositol decreased, indicating that the compound was only able to replace structural water to any great extent when the latter was removed by desiccation. To perform such a protective function the compound must combine with the vital structure damaged and either physically prevent any distortion of the structure or suppress the migration of exitation energy (Fig. 4-14). The results of this series of experiments on viability loss and inositol protection made it more apparent that bound water played a very vital structural role in maintaining the biological integrity of macromolecules. The fact that x-ray damage was more severe at 70 per cent RH than at lower or higher RH values, which was the complete reverse of that found for UV or desiccation alone, all seemed to support our hypotheses.

As we had done for desiccation and UV we went through the various metabolic activities of the cell including mutant frequen-

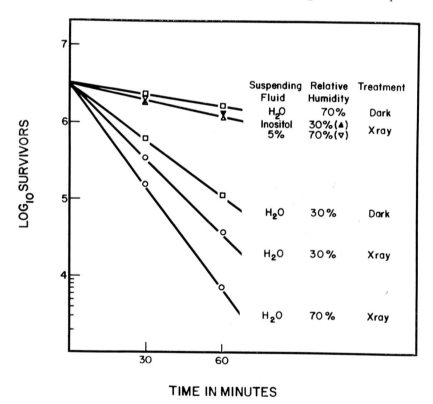

TIME IN MINUTES

Figure 4-14 The effect of RH and inositol on the death of air-borne *E. coli* in dark aerosols and when irradiated with x-rays for sixty minutes at 15r/minute.

cies, phage capacity loss and vegetative phage inactivation, as well as the induction of lysis in *E. coli K12*. From the reader's point of view, it would be sheer monotony to plough through this data for the same type of results were obtained with x-ray as with UV and desiccation. The only difference was that the RH picture was reversed. Maximal inactivation of the "capacity" and vegetative phage, maximal mutant frequencies but minimal lysis of lysogenic *K12* all occurred at around 70 per cent RH instead of the low humidities, but despite this reversal, inositol prevented all of these phenomena from taking place.

**The Modifying Action of Added Chemicals**

In Chapter 2, the action of various compounds on the viability of air-borne cells was discussed and as the work progressed, more strength was added to our original hypothesis that inositol, because of its structural similarity to water, acted as water when the cells were desiccated. Other compounds such as sodium arsenite and various cyclic compounds with substituted amine or hydroxyl groups were also found to protect but often their protection was evident only at low humidities and most were toxic to the cells at high humidities. The fact that x-ray was most lethal at 70 per cent RH gave us an added method of examining various compounds as protective agents against all three physical agents at various levels of RH. The compounds chosen were sodium arsenite; thiourea, since this has been repeatedly reported as a radiation protector; 2-amino resorcinol; inositol and dimethylsulphoxide (DMS). The latter compound was selected as it has recently received much attention as a protective agent for frozen animal cells (Lovelock and Bishop, 1959; Dougherty, 1962) and our own thoughts at this time were turning towards the similarity between our findings with bacteria and viruses and the occasional reports on both plant and animal cells, especially with respect to the so-called "early" proteins.

At 70 per cent RH and above, all of the tested compounds with the exception of inositol proved to be toxic to the cells in un-irradiated (Dark) aerosols, whereas at 30 per cent RH all were protective with DMS apparently slightly superior to any other. Their ability to prevent 2357 A UV damage, however, showed a considerable dependence on the RH at which the cells were held. Each compound displayed its maximum protective action at 30 per cent RH and all but inositol were unable to prevent damage at 70 per cent RH. It was interesting to find that 2-amino resorcinol afforded the cells a better degree of protection at 30 per cent RH than any other compound but was the most toxic at 70 per cent RH. The greatest difference between the protective ability of these chemical additives was found when they were used in conjunction with x-rays. Thiourea, inositol and 2-aminoresorcinol were extremely effective stabilizers at 30 per cent RH, whereas DMS and sodium arsenite were completely inactive. However, at 70 per cent RH only inositol proved able to prevent x-ray damage and at 90 per cent RH its protective ability was reduced. As far as the x-ray data were concerned, it was apparent that with the exception of DMS, x-rays were unable to add to the toxic action of these chemicals at 70 per cent RH, indicating that toxicity and x-ray damage were caused by the same processes. In addition, the death rate of x-irradiated cells at 30 per cent RH in the presence of DMS or sodium arsenite had almost the same value as that of cells irradiated at 70 per cent RH in water or in the presence of thiourea in dark aerosols. These facts indicated also a common mechanism by which these chemical and physical agents killed cells.

**The Mechanism by Which Added Chemicals Modify Radiation Damage**

Under the experimental conditions described it would appear that with the exception of DMS, x-rays are unable to increase the death rate over and above that produced by toxic chemicals at 70 per cent RH, and since chemical toxicity is dependent on the RH it must also be related to the bound water content of the cell. Thus it would appear that toxic action of these chemicals at high humidities results from their ability to compete with water for sites on macromolecules. In so doing, they will remove or reorientate water molecules and form hydrated structures which through hydrogen bonds or even covalent links across a double bond distort the structure of nucleoproteins. It may be argued that the bulk of the x-ray damage is produced in the same way, for if it were not so, then one would expect the $K_R$ value of cells aerosolized from water at 70 per cent RH to be superimposed on the $K_D$ values of cells aerosolized at 70 per cent RH from thiourea or 2-aminoresorcinol. Thus the death rate in the case of cells atomized in thiourea and x-rayed would be 0.097 + 0.078 or 0.175. This, however, is not the case. An alternative explanation could be based on the difference between the $K_R$ and $K_D$ values of thiourea-irradiated cells. At both 30 and 70 per cent RH this difference has a constant low value of 0.003 and it could be argued that thiourea, although toxic at the higher RH levels, prevents further damage by the x-rays. However, if this were the case the compound must have displaced the bound water apparently responsible for the x-ray damage. In any event, both explanations lead to the conclusion that toxicity results from the hydration of chemical additives and the "water addition" products are toxic structures which, when attached to vital macromolecules, destroy the integrity of the latter. Therefore, it seems reasonable to assume that the re-orientation of the bound water molecules by thiourea or 2-aminoresorcinol at 70 per cent RH is as lethal as that produced by the x-rays themselves, moreover, the same water molecules, or rather the same sites, appear to be affected, otherwise the $K_D$ values in the presence of a toxic compound and the $K_R$ values of water atomized cells should be additive. The above hypothesis is strengthened by the demonstration that DMS and sodium arsenite at 30 per cent RH will not prevent x-ray damage although both are protective in the dark. This appears to be due to the ability of both compounds to prevent inactivation in the dark by retaining cellular water rather than replacing it and their toxicity at high RH is assumed to be due to the kind of hydrated structures they form. Inositol will form hydration products similar in structure to those of water blocks and will be desiccated by low RH levels, hence it should not display any toxic action and this is exactly what is found. To test these assumptions we aerosolized cells from mixtures of inositol plus DMS or sodium arsenite and in every case, these compounds interfered with the protective action of inositol, both in the dark and under UV or x-radiation, but there was also a concomitant reduction in their toxicity indicating that addition products formed presumably through hydro-

gen bonds between these compounds and inositol (Webb and Dumasia, 1964). Inositol is not an antioxidant and yet is a very efficient
radiation protector, both against x-rays and UV, and it is evident
from the presented studies that even if an oxygen effect is involved
in x-ray damage, inositol will prevent it by some means other
than an antioxidation process. The ease with which oxygen is
excited by radiations is well known and it can only be assumed
that the added effect of oxygen sometimes found in x-ray studies
is due to the hydration of the radiation products of oxygen by
bound water.

As far as UV light is concerned it seems quite clear that water
itself is protective while the free groups of a macromolecule are
all hydrated, however, when they are not, the water itself may
become toxic by its re-orientation. Therefore, any compound
able to replace the water correctly will maintain the essential
structure of vital macromolecules under stress from desiccation
or UV light. It is clear also that compounds toxic to cells at high
RH are not protective at these levels because they themselves re-
orientate water and the UV light helps them to achieve this (Table
4-IV). These facts support the notion that it is the type of hydrated structures formed that determine whether the compound will
protect or destroy a cell. Presumably thiourea and 2-aminore-
sorcinol form toxic hydrated structures only when certain limited
amounts of water are available for both compounds will protect
cells either at very low water content levels (30 per cent RH) or
when the cells are suspended in water. In the latter case, however,
the maximum protection is never greater than a factor of ten,
whereas factors of over 1000 can be achieved in aerosols at 30 per
cent RH. Presumably the very high levels of protection possible in
aerosols is due to the extreme sensitivity of semi-dried cells in
aerosols even at relative humidities of 70 per cent or above, as
compared with cells in aqueous suspensions. Undoubtedly, the
large amounts of water present make it difficult for the light to
kill but also prevent the protective chemical from attaching itself
correctly to macromolecules. From the standpoint of the target
theory, it was interesting to find that the "hit" number of cells
protected with hydroxycyclohexanes seemed to coincide with the
number of -OH groups. This is shown clearly in Figure 4-10, for

TABLE 4-IV

The Effect of Added Chemicals on the Death Rate of Desiccated
and Irradiated *E. coli* B with Respect to Relative Humidity

| Chemical Added | RH | Desiccation Alone ($K_I$) | Ultraviolet Light 2537A 1.2x10⁴ergs/cm² (4 min. exposure) | X-ray for One Hour 15r/min. |
|---|---|---|---|---|
| Inositol (5%) | 30 | 0.006* | 73.6 (99) # | 0.007* |
| | 70 | 0.005 | 75.4 (99) | 0.007 |
| Thiourea (1.0%) | 30 | 0.012 | 74.8 (94) | 0.015 |
| | 70 | 0.078 | 44.2 (86) | 0.082 |
| 2-amino-resorcinol (1.0%) | 30 | 0.003 | 84.3 (99) | 0.008 |
| | 70 | 0.140 | 38.6 (72) | 0.113 |
| Dimethyl-sulphoxide (5.0%) | 30 | 0.004 | 72.4 (98) | 0.083 |
| | 70 | 0.049 | 52.4 (91) | 0.084 |
| Sodium arsenite (1.0%) | 30 | 0.031 | 63.7 (94) | 0.082 |
| | 70 | 0.072 | 0.8 (89) | 0.084 |
| Nil | 30 | 0.046 | 0.1 (93) | 0.075 |
| | 70 | 0.005 | 61.2 (99) | 0.097 |

\* Death rate calculated from $N_t = N_o e^{-Kt}$ expressed in minutes $^{-1}$

\# Since the death rate is not exponential the UV results are expressed in percentage viable recovery. The figures in brackets represent the viable recovery in dark aerosols after five minutes with the added chemicals.

inositol and trihydroxycyclohexane protected cells. The former gave a hit number of approximately six and the latter three. Moreover, cells dried from water at 80 per cent RH at the same dose rate indicated a hit number of three, while at the low dose rate the number was close to six (Fig. 4-9). We feel, therefore, reasonably confident that the multiplicity changes observed with wet cells as the intensity is altered are due entirely to the need to rupture H-bonds between water and the macromolecules, or in the case of inositol, between it and the vital structure before the latter is damaged.

## Summary and Conclusions

It is evident from these studies that a drastic change in the radiation sensitivity of a cell or virus occurs when the bound water content is changed. Moreover, this change occurs quite sharply at

70 per cent RH with the cells most resistant to UV or any other higher wavelength of light at the high humidities but more sensitive to x-rays. In addition, various properties of the cells such as their ability to manufacture phages and adaptive enzymes follows exactly the same RH pattern, and so does the radio-sensitivity of intracellular vegetative phages or prophages. The only change in function of the cell, due to drying or irradiation, found to display a slightly different reaction to alterations in RH was the mutation frequency. Throughout our experiments maximal numbers of mutant cells were found at 40 per cent RH which contrasts a little with the results of Kaplan and Kaplan (1956). The latter workers demonstrated clearly that the number of UV induced S-mutant cells of *Serratia marcescens* increased rapidly below 75 per cent RH and maximal numbers occurred at 33 per cent RH. Why this minor difference should exist is not clear but it is just possible that, in the aerosol, the added sensitivity of the cells to UV over those on filters is a contributing factor or that the induction of some mutations responds differently to RH changes. In any event, it is evident that bound water plays an important role in modifying the frequency with which UV induced mutants appear and its action is manifested only during the irradiation. The addition of bound water after irradiation apparently does not influence the mutant frequency. (Kaplan and Kaplan, 1956).

Ionizing radiations are known to react with water molecules but from our experiments, it would seem that the ionization of water is lethal only if it occurs in one of the bound water molecules or near enough to one of the latter so that it hydrates the formed ions. Moreover, under our experimental conditions, the bulk of x-ray damage appears to be caused by the removal or reorientation of bound water and the subsequent formation of unnatural water addition products as well as intra or inter molecular bonds irreversible with water. The same seems true of ultraviolet damage although the action of bound water can be protective. Some workers (Webb, R. B., 1963) have reported that x-ray damage increases with decreasing water content of the cells. However, no effort on the part of the above workers was made to determine how much water was removed or from what molecules.

Moreover, the vapour pressures studied ranged from $10^{-1}$ mm. Hg down to $10^{-5}$ mm., and from a biological point of view such vapour pressures are meaningless as far as bound water is concerned. At such low vapour pressures only compounds such as $P_2O_5$ can retain water while sulphuric acid, phosphates or sulphates cannot. In addition, these low vapour pressures can bring about the removal of water by the disruption of co-valent $-H$ and $-OH$ groups from organic molecules. The increase in death rate of x-irradiated cells as vapour pressures below 1.0 mm. is, therefore, most likely the result of the absorption of x-rays in molecules strained by low vapour pressures and the radiant energy helps to rupture co-valently held $-H$ and $-OH$ groups from the large macromolecules. Under these circumstances, adsorped water is not being studied for no biological molecule will retain water at these low vapour pressures.

The protective action of inositol, thiourea, and 2-aminoresorcinol, as well as water, when the cell macromolecules are fully hydrated, seems to rely on their ability to suppress the migration of excitation energy or alter the direction in which the energy travels and their action as structural pillars preventing the distortion of the nucleoproteins. We can, therefore, look upon radiations as molecular desiccants, just as are toxic chemicals and desiccation itself for the latter does not kill until the bound water is affected. With this hypothesis in mind, we have recently examined the formation of thymine dimers in aerosolized cells killed by low doses of radiation at 30 and 60 per cent RH. This we did by growing the thymine deficient cells in a full medium plus $C^{14}$ thymine. The collected cells were concentrated in small vials and hydrolysed with perchloric acid in an autoclave, neutralized, the hydrolysate chromatographed, and the radio-active spots detected by passing the strips through an automatic Nuclear Chicago strip counter equipped with an integrater. It was interesting to find that although the death rate at 60 per cent RH and 30 per cent RH was the same, no thymine dimers were detected at 60 per cent RH and only a very small percentage, amounting to 0.04 per cent of the total thymine, was found at 30 per cent RH. Since one cannot kill a cell twice, we concluded that the dimer was a result of death and is produced under conditions of high dose rates or dryness where the action of bound water goes unnoticed. The fact that the amount of thymine dimer under our experimental conditions appears to be dependent on the bound water content of a cell at the time of irradiation, and not the number of cells killed, is taken to mean that many cells die as a result of the production of lethal water addition products. The less bound water present in a cell, the more easily these will be produced. Moreover, it is unnecessary for them to be formed across a double bond in order that they be lethal. Lethal water re-orientation is most likely to occur at about 55 per cent RH and below when the $=P=O$, $=C=O$ groups are hydrated, whereas the -N, -NH, -NH$_2$ and -OH groups are not. The x-ray results tend to suggest that the ionization of a bound water molecule attached to one of the latter groups is more likely to be lethal than the ionization of water adsorbed to the former groups, although it is possible for water orientated by hydrophobic groups to be involved. The fact that none of the photo-products of thymine or uracil is capable of supporting the growth of thymine or uracil dependent mutants (Wacker, 1963) in itself suggests the water addition products to be biologically of great significance and at the same time suggests that enzymes capable of breaking down radiation products do not occur naturally. We cannot, of course, be dogmatic about our inability to find thymine dimers at 60 per cent RH, for we do not know for sure how many dimers are necessary to kill a cell, if in fact they are responsible for death. There is always the possibility that only one per cell is needed, in which case, even by the sensitive RA technique, we may not be able to detect them.

Some cells undoubtedly die as a result of inter or intra molecular reactions between the desiccated groups of macromolecules and the subsequent formation of DNA or RNA base polymers. However, the very large doses of UV needed to produce thymine dimers in isolated DNA and the fact that only one thymine molecule in 1000 dimerized after a dose sufficient to kill 99 per cent of the cells (Wacker, 1963), make it seem unlikely that this dimer alone causes death. It is much more likely that most of the dimers found with the large doses usually used are produced in cells already dead.

As far as the target theory is concerned, the change in multiplicity with "wetness" or, more correctly, bound water content, is readily explainable. If the dose rate is sufficient to affect six water molecules at a time then one will obtain either an exponential survival versus time, or dose, plot or a low multiplicity. On the other hand, if the dose rate is sufficient to affect only one water molecule within a given time, in a dynamic system a removed water molecule can be replaced from the atmosphere and obviously multiplicities are going to increase. The findings with inositol would suggest that all six -OH groups have to be displayed at once, for a constant hit number of about six is always found by the extrapolation of the multi-hit curve obtained with this compound under conditions of dose rate where its protectiveness breaks down. This kind of argument is supported by the described experiments with trihydroxycyclohexane. We feel, therefore, that if the hydration is taken into account the target theory does describe the happenings inside a cell during irradiation but the multiplicities observed may have nothing to do with ploidy or metabolic control by one or more genes, they may very well indicate the degree of hydration or the kind of compounds such as sugars, lipids, polyalcohols or polyamines, attached to the DNA or RNA molecules. Also, as shown, the type of organism used and the density of cells on filters or in aqueous suspension can change not only the kind of log survival versus dose curve obtained, but also the multiplicity. Thus it is possible with organisms such as *Staphylococcus* or yeasts that observed multiplicities may be due to clumping. *E. coli* is not a clumping organism, but in recent experiments utilizing aerosols containing from 1 to 20 cells per drop we have observed the same drop in x-ray sensitivity with increasing numbers of cells per drop, previously observed with UV. Since these clumps break up during collection in the impinger and single cells are subsequently counted, some protection against x-rays due to cell-to-cell contact in the droplet nuclei must occur. This seems difficult to reconcile with the penetrating powers of x-rays, but if the water alone can offer a measure of protection, the orientation of macromolecules within a cell, its proximity to other molecules, and the packing of the cells themselves may all determine the ultimate total response of a population to x-rays. In the aerosol drum, the average dose rate was calculated to be about 15r/minute. This means that during one hour of irradiation the airborne cells received approximately 900r yet 99 per cent of the cells held at 70 per cent RH were killed. To produce the same number of deaths on filters or in aqueous suspensions some 10 to 15 Kr are required so it would appear that cells are from ten to fifteen times more sensitive to x-rays when irradiated in aerosols than when treated in aqueous suspension or in multilayers on filters. This could indicate a pronounced protective action of free water. In any event, the added sensitivity simulates the findings with ultraviolet light where airborne cells were found to be from ten to twenty times more sensitive to the radiations than those held in suspensions. In addition, some recent experiments conducted by Dr. D. V. Cormack of the physics department has indicated that dose-rate may be important in determining the extent of x-ray damage. When 200 to 300 cells of *S. marcescens* are dispersed on millipore filters, dried, irradiated, and the colonies allowed to develop on the filters, the death versus RH in the dark simulates that of the aerosol, and so does the protection by inositol. However, the effect of RH on x-ray damage although very pronounced is slightly different, and the ability of inositol to prevent radiation damage is reduced. The dose rate used by Dr. Cormack is about 600r/minute, so RH effects and inositol protection appear to be altered by x-ray dose-rate, just as they are by the rate at which cells are irradiated with ultraviolet light. It naturally follows that experiments with x-rays integrating dose rate, RH and inositol effects should be carried out and we have been extremely fortunate to have just obtained a new x-ray apparatus with which this type of experiment can be conducted.

It may be argued that damage to either DNA or RNA results in cell death because of the greater stability of *E. coli B* phage capacity or the prophage in *E. coli* K12 over that of the cell itself towards UV and x-rays. On the other hand, since the vegetative phages in infected cells are almost as sensitive as their host at the onset of infection, it seems more likely that damage to any part of the host DNA will result in the loss of colony forming ability, whereas damage must occur in a relatively small part of the DNA to inactivate the prophage. This will require larger doses or lower water content. In addition, if the vegetative phage required all the host DNA to be intact at the onset of infection, then the smaller doses will make it impossible for the virus to multiply. As far as the T-even phages are concerned, some explanation is needed to answer the question as to why the host cell capacity remains intact under UV irradiation but the vegetative phage early in its development does not. We offer the suggestion that part of the internal protein injected into the host with the viral DNA affixes itself to host RNA, blocking RNA and protein synthesis and the naked viral DNA is now more easily damaged. The fact that the mature virus is so sensitive to UV may be due to completely different reasons, namely the close packing of the DNA in the viral head rendering group to group contact more easily achieved, or the lack of bound water.

It can be seen from the various figures that a dose of $4.5 \times 10^4$/ergs./cm$^2$ of 2800 to 3200 A light, or $1.0 \times 10^4$/ergs./cm$^2$ of 2537 A radiation is sufficient to reduce the viable count by three orders of magnitude at 30 per cent RH. This is about twenty times less than that needed to inactivate the same number of cells in solutions, and about fifteen times less than that needed to kill dry bacterial spores (Setlow and Pollard, 1962). The reason for the former is obviously the stabilization of the cells by water molecules but as for the latter, the reason is not clear. Possibly the spore coat allows less light to penetrate than does the cell wall, or alternatively, the monodispersal of cells in the aerosol prevents protection due to layers of cells.

Our hypothesis as to the action of bound water is schematically outlined in Fig. 4-15. It is suggested that the structure of large conjugate macromolecules relies on the presence of correctly orientated bound water molecules and that some of the latter are concerned in both intra and inter molecular structure. It follows that since x-rays will attack these water molecules directly, its lethal action will be more pronounced at high humidities, especially when only a monolayer exists. On the other hand, with UV, energy migrations are needed to displace water and hence, the more molecules present the more difficult this becomes, particularly if displaced ones are quickly replaced from the environment.

The stabilizing action of inositol against x-ray is thought to be due to the stability of the saturated six-carbon ring as opposed to the H-bonded rings formed by water molecules. While one "hit" on the latter is sufficient to rupture the whole water ring complex, such would not be the case with inositol, for this compound is notoriously stable to heat and radiations. Moreover, since inositol is not an antioxidant the mechanism by which it protects cells must be something other than an antioxidation process.

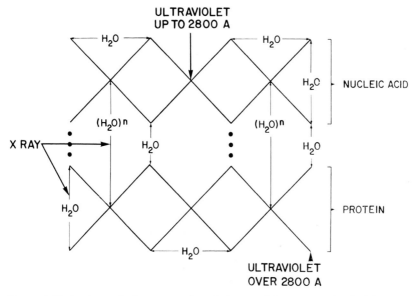

Figure 4-15 A schematic interpretation of the possible structural role of water molecules in a conjugate nucleoprotein molecule and how the complete structure may be affected by desiccation and the absorption of various radiations (taken from Webb, *Nature 201*, 1964).

Even though it was by way of an accident, perhaps one of the most significant of our findings was the action of non-lethal doses of 3000 to 4000 A light on adaptive enzyme and virus synthesis. This led us to investigate the rates of protein, RNA and DNA synthesis in starved cells, presumably synchronized as far as their metabolic processes were concerned. We do not believe the two phases of RNA and protein synthesis observed, or the apparent necessity for the amino acids to build up to a desired level before DNA replication occurs, to be artifacts of starvation. More likely, the straight line relationships found by many other workers with logarithmically growing cells are the result of fast growing unsynchronized cultures. As pointed out in the previous chapter, this rapid uptake of aminoacids during the first fifteen minutes shows a remarkable resemblance to that found in plant and animal cells where the incorporation appears to take place in the nucleus and on the DNA. The action of the "black light" in preventing adaptive enzyme synthesis or virus production provided the cells are irradiated immediately and its complete failure to stop these processes after fifteen minutes of incubation in the appropriate medium is so much like the findings on the stability of vegetative phage, adaptive enzyme or virus producing capacity toward lethal doses of x-ray or UV that it can hardly be a coincidence. Moreover, the demonstration that the uptake of basic aminoacids is the most affected by "black light" suggests the formation of some basic protein on the DNA not only stabilizes it, but is responsible for it undergoing replication, for if the aminoacid uptake is suppressed, little thymine uptake occurs. Obviously there must be two methods or two sequences of protein synthesis for the light does not affect the subsequent formation of adaptive enzymes or the synthesis of viral coat protein, possibly because it does not interfere with cytoplasmic RNA synthesis or the proteins synthesized by the cytoplasmic RNA.

At the conclusion of these works, we felt that the action of desiccation, toxic chemicals and radiations could all be explained, in part, by the phenomenon we chose to call "molecular desiccation." Our work, however, had been basically theoretical and one is always hoping for some practical application of the work to appear. One of the main problems confronting biologists today is that of cancer, and as our work progressed, it became more and more evident that the action of carcinogens, radiations and even old age, could be explained as a result of molecular desiccation, particularly as many of the carcinogenic compounds were found to protect bacterial cells and were bacteriostatic. Therefore, I contacted our Cancer Research Unit and explained the idea and with the aid of Dr. R. Bather we began to experiment with animal cells, normal and malignant. The results have been very encouraging and are outlined in the next chapter.

# CHAPTER 5

# BOUND WATER AND ANIMAL CELLS

## The Stability of Dry and Non-dried Cells

A S A RESULT OF THE WORK DESCRIBED on bacteria and viruses, the idea was formulated that changes in animal cells due to bound water loss might occur and that these could lead to the development of malignant cells (Webb, 1963a). Experiments were commenced, therefore, on the effects of desiccation on animal cells both from the standpoint of stability, virus release and mutation. First amnion cells were studied (Webb, Bather and Cook, 1963) and later, other kinds of cells. For simplicity of reading, the results have been pooled and do not necessarily follow the same experimental time sequence as suggested by the text. In fact, most of the experiments were started at the same time, but some results came more quickly than others.

Chick embryos ten to twelve days old, spleens from normal one to two month old chickens or two to three month-old Swiss mice, and thymuses from the same animals were suspended in Hank's balanced salt solution (BSS) to make an approximate 1:10 tissue fluid mixture. This mixture was homogenized for 1.0 minute at low speed, the homogenate strained through twelve layers of surgical gauze and centrifuged at 2000 rpm for ten minutes. On re-suspension, these cells were found to be singly dispersed and easily countable. Ehrlich ascites cells, chromosome No. 78 and subline SN576 were harvested from diseased animals, centrifuged, washed once in BSS and re-suspended in BSS or 5 per cent inositol. Tissue cultures were carried out in 60 mm. Petri dishes incubated in a humidified chamber flushed with 95 per cent air–5 per cent $CO_2$ mixture. Mouse and chick embryo

134

and amnion cells were trypsinized in BSS containing 0.25 per cent trypsin and the cells grown in medium 199 supplemented with 5 per cent calf serum and 2.5 per cent calf embryo extract.

Since the cells would not stand aerosolization, drying of embryo or amnion cells in the Petri dishes was carried out in a cabinet through which air of a controlled humidity could be passed. The cells on the plates were allowed to grow and surplus cells removed by washing with fresh medium. The number of growing cells was scored a day later, the medium removed and the cells washed in the petri plates with either BSS or 5 per cent inositol. The washing fluid was then removed and the cells transferred to the drying cabinet and dried for thirty minutes at various RH levels. Fresh medium was then added, the cells reincubated for two days and the number of cells still able to grow was determined.

Cells held at 80 per cent RH seemed unaffected by the drying but at 70 per cent or lower few survived as far as their ability to grow was concerned even in inositol. However, it was apparent that more survived in inositol although their numbers were extremely small amounting to about 0.01 per cent. Shorter drying times allowed more to survive and up to 5 per cent to 10 per cent of the cells grew after drying in inositol at 40 per cent RH for ten minutes, whereas only 0.05 per cent survived when dried in BSS.

During the course of these studies, it was noticed that cell suspensions made in inositol seemed to grow better than those made in BSS and so a study was made of the stability of various cell types held in solution in BSS or 5 per cent inositol. Initially, the permeability of the cells to erythrosin was examined using an equal number of cells in equal volumes of BSS or 5 per cent inositol. In a total of thirty experiments, the cells incubated in inositol showed better viability as measured by lack of permeability to erythrosin than did those incubated in BSS. In most cases, the viability after incubation in inositol was 100 per cent or very close to it (Table 5-I).

Since Ehrlich ascites cells are easily available in large quantities these were chosen for some respiration studies after the cells

TABLE 5-I
ERYTHROSIN STAINING PROPERTIES OF VARIOUS CELLS
AFTER INCUBATION IN BSS OR 5% INOSITOL AT 37°C.

| Cells* | Incubation (hr.) | % Cells Remaining Unstained Incubated in BSS | % Cells Remaining Unstained Incubated in 5% Inositol |
|---|---|---|---|
| Mouse spleen (8) | ¼-3 | 50-90 | 91-100 |
| Mouse thymus (2) | 1-2 | 52,64 | 92,97 |
| Chicken spleen (7) | 1-2 | 29-84 | 62-100 |
| Chick embryo (3) | 1-3 | 6-64 | 85-100 |
| Ehrlich ascites (10) | 1-3 | 24-70 | 69-97 |

*Numbers in parentheses indicate the number of observations made.

had been stored for ninety minutes in BSS or 5 per cent inositol at 37°C., washed and re-suspended in phosphate buffer. Table 5-II summarizes the results of experiments and also includes the data on erythrocin staining properties of the cells immediately before transferring them to the Warburg flasks. Total cell counts indicated that the number of cells in each Warburg flask was within 10 per cent in each individual experiment. The oxygen uptake of the cells incubated in inositol was higher in every experiment and was similar to the control non-incubated cells in BSS or inositol. The possibility that cells were metabolizing residual inositol was ruled out by adding 1.0 per cent inositol to the Warburg flasks and observing no difference in the respiration rate. As a final test, we examined the ability of embryo cells to grow in tissue cultures. In our first experiments established cells three days

TABLE 5-II
ERYTHROSIN STAINING AND OXYGEN UPTAKE OF EHRLICH ASCITES
CELLS PREINCUBATED FOR 90 MINUTES IN BSS OR 5% INOSITOL

| Expt. No. | % Cells Remaining Unstained* BSS | % Cells Remaining Unstained* 5% inositol | Oxygen Uptake (µl/hour) of Cells Preincubated in BSS | Oxygen Uptake (µl/hour) of Cells Preincubated in 5% inositol |
|---|---|---|---|---|
| 1 | 43 | 69 | 65 | 104 |
| 2 | 60 | 97 | 62 | 110 |
| 3 | 39 | 72 | 27 | 126 |
| 4 | 70 | 95 | 69 | 134 |
| 5 | 59 | 92 | 68 | 173 |
| 6 | 68 | 91 | 78 | 114 |
| 7 | 56 | 86 | 60 | 94 |
| 8 | — | — | 140 | 159 |

* Erythrosin staining was determined after the cells had been preincubated in BSS or inositol, centrifuged, and resuspended in buffer for transfer to the Warburg flasks.
8 is control non-incubated cells.

old in 2 oz. bottles were washed in BSS or inositol, incubated for three hours in BSS or inositol, the latter two solutions removed and fresh medium added. After one week, this procedure was carried out again and repeated over a four week period. In both cases, the cells appeared unaffected by the treatment, they grew well, peeled off and reseeded themselves. In later experiments, a cell suspension containing approximately $10^3$ chick embryo cells/ ml. was made either in inositol or BSS and immediately 0.5 ml. placed into large petri dishes in 10.0 ml. of growth medium. The cell suspensions were kept at room temperature and 0.5 ml. aliquots placed in the dishes and growth medium at one hour, five hour and ten hour intervals. The cells were then incubated at 37°C for thirty-six hours and the number of cells showing growth scored. We later repeated this same experiment but stored the cells at 4°C. or at −20°C., and results shown in Table 5-III show clearly that while inositol preserved the viability of the cells at room temperature and at 4°C. it did little to help the cells at −20°C. At first, we thought this was due to freezing damage but experiments being carried out at the present time seem to indicate that the same phenomenon occurs with tumor viruses stored in inositol. Apparently, infectivity of the suspension is maintained for up to ten days in inositol at 4°C., but drops very rapidly at

TABLE 5-III

THE ABILITY OF INOSITOL TO PRESERVE THE VIABILITY
OF CHICK-EMBRYO CELLS AT VARIOUS TEMPERATURES

| Temperature | | Time of Storage | | | | | |
|---|---|---|---|---|---|---|---|
| | | 1 Hour | 5 Hours | 10 Hours | 24 Hours | 3 Days | 7 Days |
| 37°C | I | 95 | 88 | 68 | 42 | nil | nil |
| | B | 47 | 8 | nil | nil | nil | nil |
| 25°C | I | 98 | 84 | 77 | 58 | 6 | nil |
| | B | 68 | 12 | 4 | nil | nil | nil |
| 4°C | I | 98 | 92 | 88 | 80 | 42 | 2 |
| | B | 74 | 52 | 8 | 3 | nil | nil |
| −20°C | I | — | — | 2 | nil | nil | nil |
| | B | — | — | 21 | 18 | nil | nil |

I = 5% inositol.
B = BSS.
Results expressed as a percentage of the control cells
able to grow on subsequent seeding into Petri dishes.

−20°C. There would seem to be some biophysical phenomenon operative at this temperature for it has been known for some time that frozen bacteria also lose their viability rapidly around this temperature.

One explanation would seem to lie in the physical properties of bound water for it is known that these molecules do not freeze until temperatures of around −20°C. are reached. In other words, their physico-chemical structure remains the same as water, not ice, down to −20°C. However, this idea very quickly received a set back when Dr. S. Fedoroff of our department of anatomy used inositol instead of DMS or Glycerol to preserve cells frozen in liquid nitrogen. Apparently, all but Hela cells responded well to inositol and the latter compound appeared as efficient in preserving cells at liquid nitrogen temperatures as DMS and far better than glycerol. Possibly the inability of inositol to preserve cells at −20°C. is something to do with the change in structure of bound water and its association with inositol. Possibly those water molecules attached to the macromolecular groups of cell components change physically at −20°C., whereas those −HOH groups of inositol, also attached to the cell component, do not. This would result in a stress on the macromolecule and damage may occur in the same way as toxic chemicals appear to operate in bacteria aerosolized at high humidities. In any event, inositol will preserve cells at 25°C. for a few hours and at 4°C. for longer periods of time as well as at liquid nitrogen temperatures (Fedoroff, personal communication).

### The Effect of Bound Water Loss on the Synthesis and Release of Viruses and Nucleic Acids

In the experiments described above, it was noticed that when cells were incubated in inositol the suspensions were invariably a little more viscous than the BSS suspensions and the cells were more difficult to disperse. On examination by microscope, it was noticed that the cells appeared more transparent in inositol than in BSS. In the light of previous observations with dried bacteria and the release of nucleic acids, we decided to examine the supernatant of inositol and BSS suspended cells. Accordingly, many supernatant fluids from embryo, chick and mouse spleen, amnion and Ehrlich cells were examined by UV spectroscopy. In every case, the inositol supernatants absorbed more strongly at 260 m$\mu$ than did the BSS supernatants. Since the UV absorption spectrum suggested the presence of other substances other than nucleic acids some of the extracts were precipitated overnight at 4°C. with two volumes of 95 per cent ethanol. The precipitates were then extracted with 10 per cent NaCl for thirty minutes at 100°C. The resulting extracts were again read in the UV spectrophotometer at 260 m$\mu$. The phenomenon of increased release of UV absorbing material in the presence of inositol was more noticeable with the purified material with differences of from ten to 100 times that found in BSS extracts. A typical example is shown in Fig. 5-1. Perhaps of greater significance was the fact that the relative differences in amount of absorbing material released in inositol compared with that in BSS was much greater with normal cells than with tumor cells, in fact with some of the latter little difference could be found. This coupled with the inability of inositol to protect certain types of tumor cells would seem to suggest that a difference exists in the structure of the nucleic acids of the two types of cell. In normal cells apparently inositol can combine intra or intermolecularly with cell RNA and possibly DNA, whereas in the tumor cell it cannot. Such findings indicate that the DNA and RNA of tumor cells are much tighter structures and possibly have less sites available to water. This idea is discussed later and certainly requires further investigations.

Estimates of the relative proportions of the bases, made by Dr. Bather (Bather, Webb and Sebastian, 1964) revealed no evidence of base pairing of the Watson and Crick type, but in all cases a predominance of purines over pyrimidines was apparent. Moreover, the ratio of 6-keto groups to 6-amino groups in all samples was approximately one (0.86 to 1.03). One important point with respect to the RNA lost from these cells was a marked asymmetry of the base composition of the RNA released particularly between the Ehrlich tumor and sublime SN576 derived from the former. Some of these differences in base ratios were as follows: For chicken spleen the adenine to guanine ratio was 1:1.06; Ehrlich

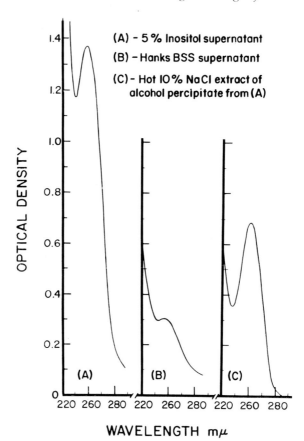

WAVELENGTH mµ

Figure 5-1 Ultraviolet absorption curves of the supernatant fluids from normal chicken spleen cells incubated for 2 hours in (A) 5 per cent inositol or (B) Hanks' BSS. Curve C is the UV absorption curve of a hot (100°C. for thirty minutes) 10 per cent sodium chloride extract of the material precipitated by the addition of two volumes of ethanol to the supernatant fluid from (A). All solutions were diluted ten-fold for reading in the Beckmann DB spectrophotometer (taken from Bather, Webb and Sebastian, *Canad. J. Biochem., 42, 1964*).

1:1.48; SN 576 1:2.12; and cytosine to uracil 0.61: 0.51; 0.99: 0.68; and 1.66: 0.72 respectively.

At this stage of the work, it became increasingly clear that a large amount of cell RNA is unnecessary and that one of the actions of inositol was to purge this material from the cell. As with bacteria the release of this material seemed to be a protective function rather than a reason for death. Apparently, the change in permeability of the cells in inositol allowed the release of RNA but suppressed the uptake of dye. If one could obtain large molecular weight nucleoproteins it seemed reasonable to suppose that some viruses might also be released. This was first tested with tissue cultures infected with adeno-virus or Rous sarcoma viruses and later with both solid and ascites tumor tissue induced in chickens by injection of Rous cells. In every case, more viruses were obtained in the inositol supernatants than in the BSS supernatants. However, once again referring back to lysogenic bacteria we examined the effect of drying cells on the release of virus. Tissue infected with adeno-virus or Rous tumor cells were dried with and without inositol, Ehrlich ascites cells known to carry various Murine leukemia viruses were dried with inositol. Assay for adeno-virus was made in tissue culture, for Rous sarcoma by pock counts in chick eggs and for leukemia virus by inoculating eight-week-old female mice intra-peritoneally with 0.2 ml. of the supernatant fluids filtered through a 450 m$\mu$ millipore filter. The results are shown in Table 5-IV from which it can be seen that drying the cells for thirty minutes at 60 per cent RH resulted in the release of more adeno-virus and considerably more RSV.

TABLE 5-IV
THE RELEASE OF VIRUSES ON DRYING INFECTED TISSUE
AT 60% RH AND EHRLICH ASCITES CELLS AT 40%RH

| Supernatant Filtered Fluid. | Non-dried BSS | Non-dried inositol | Dried BSS | Dried Inositol |
|---|---|---|---|---|
| Adeno virus 1 | 40 * | 160 | 80 | 640 |
| Rous sarcoma virus (RSV) | 120 ♀ | 340 | 580 | 5600 |
| Cells frozen and thawed (3x) Adeno virus | 320 | — | — | — |
| Cells frozen and thawed (3x) RSV | 2060 | — | — | — |
| Ehrlich ascites | 8-17%$^+$ | — | — | ↑ 93% |

* Titre/ml. of supernatant fluid.
♀ P.F.U./ml. of supernatant fluid.
$^+$ Range of incidence among similar sized groups of untreated mice during their lifetime.
↑ Percentage of animals developing leukemia within twelve months.

Free virus in tissue cultures or tumor tissue removed by washing once in BSS or inositol prior to drying. Titres of non-dried cells represent virus found in the supernatant after standing for thirty minutes while the others dried.

Moreover, the drying of the Ehrlich ascites cells at 40 per cent RH for thirty minutes results in 93 per cent of the animals given the filtrate developing leukemia. Some of the animals given the filtrate died with acute leukemia beginning five months after inoculation. Others were discovered at twelve months when the surviving animals were killed and autopsied. Most of the leukemias were lymphoblastic in type with large thymus tumors as well as lymphnode, liver, kidney and spleen involvement. Some of them developing later appeared to be mixed lymphoblastic lymphocytic neoplasms with cells characteristic of both types. In one case a mouse developed a typical chloroleukemia with large green lymph nodes and proliferation of myeloblasts. However, on transplantation this leukemia assumed the characteristics of lymphoblastic type. None of the animals developed ascites tumors.

The above experiments show clearly that virus in a highly active form are released from cells on drying. The presence of inositol seems to result in increased amounts of infectivity either by protecting the virus against desiccation damage as was shown earlier for RSV or by stimulating the synthesis of infectious virus from a prophage within the cell. The latter is suggested from some preliminary studies with adeno-virus I which indicate that dried cells, although unable to multiply can still manufacture virus. Again, this appears very much like the phage "capacity" of bacteria and it is planned to experiment along the same lines as that described for the phage work.

### The Possible Mutagenic Action of Bound Water Loss and the Production of Malignant Cells

Two biological phenomena associated with desiccation namely changes in function, i.e., mutation, and the release of infectious viruses led to the idea that carcinogenises might be the occasional result of such changes in animal cells. There seemed no doubt, from the work described for bacteria and viruses, that the removal of molecular bound water from the macromolecules of normal cells could result in the production of carcinogenic potentialities. Thus, the idea that desiccation might be classed with carcinogenic chemicals and radiations provided an attractive basis for a more general mechanism of carcinogenesis since all may be classified as "molecular desiccants." The removal of structural water can be accomplished by chemical means, by desiccation alone or by the various kinds of radiation. Moreover, local dehydration could result from the implantation of plastics and other so called inert material, a phenomenon known to produce tumors. Tissue desiccation in old age is well known and this could conceivably favour the conditions necessary for critical water loss. Carcinogenesis could well occur as a result of virus release or through the mutation of a viable cell on molecular desiccation. Since the latter appears to occur in microbes, we decided to examine the effect of inoculating animals with aliquots of dried cells.

Initially, pooled spleen cells from one-year-old mice were homogenized by gentle treatment and strained through gauze. After centrifugation, half the cells were suspended in BSS and the other half in inositol solution. Approximately $2 \times 10^7$ cells were placed in 60 mm. Petri dishes, allowed to settle, the supernatant fluid removed and the cells dried at 70 per cent RH for thirty minutes. The dried cells were resuspended in BSS or inositol and groups of eight-week-old Swiss mice inoculated intra-peritoneally with $5 \times 10^5$ cells. Some control groups received the same number of non-dried cells, others were given just BSS or 5 per cent inositol. The experiment was run for twelve months after which time the survivors were killed and autopsied. Sections were prepared from all animals. Since little or no difference in tumor incidence appeared between the groups treated with cells dried in BSS and those dried in inositol the groups were combined for simplicity of presentation in Table 5-V, from which it is apparent that the inoculation of dried spleen cells resulted in an increased incidence of both leukemia (lymphoblastic or mixed lymphoblastic-lymphocytic) and mammary carcinoma (Webb, 1964; Bather, Webb and Cunningham, 1964) .

It was noted in many instances that the mice receiving dried cells developed a strong plasma cell reaction with abdominal ascites formation four weeks after inoculation. This occurred in both adult or newborn mice and was usually accompanied by splenic enlargement. Although the reaction subsided over the

TABLE 5-V

INFLUENCE OF INOCULATING DRIED SPLEEN CELLS INTO SWISS MICE
(EXPERIMENT I) AND SUBSEQUENT BLIND TRANSFER OF TISSUES AT
THE HEIGHT OF "PLASMA CELL REACTION" WITHOUT DRYING (EXPERIMENT II)

| Experiment | No. of Animals | Percent Animals with Tumor | Total No. of Tumors |
|---|---|---|---|
| I.  Controls | 36 | 11 | 5  (3L, 2MC) * |
|     Non-dried cells | 24 | 8 | 4  (2L, 2MC) |
|     Dried cells | 24 | 42 | 14 (7L, 7MC) |
| II. 1st Passage | 24 | 36 | 18 (9L, 9MC) |
|     2nd Passage | 12 | 42 | 6  (5L, 1MC) |
|     3rd Passage | 18 | 56 | 10 (10L) |

* Figures in brackets indicate number of leukemias (L) and mammary carcinomas (MC).

next three weeks, marked plasma cell infiltration of lymph nodes, liver, kidney and spleen persisted until the animals were killed at the end of the experiment. Pooled ascites fluid from two mice at the height of the reaction was transferred, therefore, non-dried, to another group of eight-week-old mice and all these animals developed marked ascites and splenic enlargement within two weeks so fluid from these animals was transferred to a third group of mice with the same result. In each case, the fluids were examined both microscopically and by plating on blood agar plates for bacterial infection but none was found. These results are presented as Experiment II in Table 5-V. It is evident that the incidence of tumors increased at each passage but it was interesting to find that a high incidence of mammary carcinoma only occurred with the initial group given the dried cells, whereas the increased incidence on subsequent passage of the ascites fluid was due entirely to leukemias.

Since most of the leukemias were of the lymphoblastic type, an experiment was undertaken in which thymus cells from apparently normal two-month-old mice were dried before inoculation into new borns. In view of the bacterial mutation data suggesting 40 per cent RH to be the point at which maximal numbers of mutations occur (Webb, 1964), the cells were dried at 30 per cent or 40 per cent or 60 per cent RH in the absence of inositol but resuspended in inositol after drying. It is again evident from the results in Table 5-VI that the incidence of leukemia was greatest in the groups given cells dried at 40 per cent RH and from the final column more appeared at 60 per cent RH than in the controls, in addition, none of the animals given cells dried at 30 per cent RH developed tumors, suggesting that all biological activity was destroyed. This was not surprising in view of the results with bacteria and viruses. Another important feature of these results was that 57 per cent of the animals developing tumors in the 40 per cent dry cell group died before twelve months, the earliest (nineteen weeks) developed an ovarian carcinoma as well as leukemia, the former being an extremely rare tumor in our colony, even in old age. It is interesting also that dried thymus cells did not result in a high incidence of mammary carcinoma.

TABLE 5-VI
INCIDENCE OF TUMORS IN SWISS MICE INOCULATED WHEN
NEWBORN WITH DRIED OR NON-DRIED THYMUS CELLS

| Group | No. Animals | Percent Animals with Tumors | Total No. of Tumors |
|---|---|---|---|
| Non--dried | 15 | 26 | 4 (2L, 2MC* |
| Dried 60% RH | 17 | 24 | 5 (4L, 1MC) |
| Dried 40% RH | 13 | 60 | 9 (6L, 2MC, 1 OC) |
| Dried 30% RH | 9 | 0 | 0 |

* Figures in brackets indicate number of leukemias (L),
mammary carcinomas (MC) or ovarian carcinomas (OC).

At this time, it is not clear whether the increase in tumor incidences found is due to the release of a virus, the mutation of a cell or the appearance of an altered genetically competent macromolecule, but there seems no doubt that desiccated cells in some way will induce cancers in experimental animals. Perhaps desiccation allows intra or inter-molecular bonds to form in cell DNA, producing the tighter or more dense tumor DNA as the antioxidant data earlier suggested (Chapter 3). In any event, these results are extremely encouraging and experiments under way should throw more light on this interesting, and perhaps important, phenomenon.

# CHAPTER 6

# THE ROLE OF BOUND WATER IN THE MAINTENANCE OF THE INTEGRITY OF A CELL OR VIRUS

*That from Discussion's lips may fall*
*With Life, that, working strongly binds—*
*Set in all lights by many minds,*
*To close the interests of all.*

*For nature also, cold and warm,*
*And moist and dry, devising long,*
*Thro' many agents making strong,*
*Matures the individual form.*

TENNYSON

## A Summary of the Various Findings and Their Implications as to Cell Structure and Function

**W**ITH MOST SCIENTIFIC INVESTIGATIONS, the results of one set of experiments usually pose more questions than they answer. Certainly this was true of our endeavours. As the work progressed, numbers of new technical and scientific problems arose and the ramifications of our findings into other fields of biological research became wider. We tried to follow up our observations wherever they led, with one objective in mind, to improve our understanding of the mechanisms governing the life process, with special emphasis on the role of bound water. Wherever possible, we attempted to correlate our findings with those of others, but often it was necessary to formulate our own hypothesis and then determine whether or not we were led to the same conclusions as other workers or to different ones. Initially, there was little data with which to compare our own for, although many people had published the death rates of various air-borne

146

cells, they were not correlated with growth media, temperature and bound water content. However, as time went on and we entered the virus and radiation work, it soon became apparent that our investigations were fitting in with those of others. For instance, substances such as glycerol were found as radiation protectors; dry cells were found more resistant to x-ray than wet cells; multiplicity changes were observed between wet and dry cells as far as the target theory was concerned. Also, the early proteins in phage replication and the peculiar behaviour of vegetative phage stability with infection time were discovered. As far as most authors of these papers were concerned, these were isolated observations but to us, they began to fit into one picture with the missing piece that small but plentiful entity—water. In short, we feel we have defined "dryness," for while most workers use the term "dry" or "freeze-dried" freely, they do not know how dry, and from the investigations described it appears to be just as important from a biological point of view, in the interpretation of radiation experiments especially, to define wetness or dryness correctly as it is to measure the radiation dose. In fact, the former seems more important that the latter, for it would seem futile to go to great lengths to obtain a precise wavelength and dose and pay little heed to the age of a culture or cell, its method of growth, cell concentrations, or the conditions under which the experiment was conducted. The same, of course, is true of isolated pieces of cells as far as their structure and function is concerned. The structure of the DNA molecule itself is known to rely on bound water even outside the cell so is the structure of many proteins, yet few people have deemed it necessary to consider this an important factor inside a cell although approximately 80 per cent of the physiology of a cell relies on the movement, not of free water, but of bound water. Moreover, since the cell is in an aqueous environment every metabolite is undoubtedly hydrated and reacts with other metabolites in a hydrated form. In addition, the biologically active structure of a macromolecule *in vivo* appears to rely on the kind of association it has with other molecules and because of this there is the ever present danger that test tube experiments with cell pieces might give the very opposite reaction

to that occurring in a living cell. To take a point in question and
a typical one, the coding of aminoacids into protein by s-rna.
Most workers today assume because certain codes seem to select
a given aminoacid in the test tube that the s-rna recognizes the
messenger RNA, but an enzyme has to recognize both the aminoacid and the s-rna before the s-rna-amino acid complex is formed.
What then codes the enzyme, for presumably it cannot be made
before the complexes necessary to make it are synthesized? Such
problems as these have resulted in the creation of very complex
hypothesis as to the way the DNA code functions, and to add to
the confusion, it has recently been demonstrated that a single s-rna
molecule will incorporate a different aminoacid into a given
protein depending on the magnisium concentration. Adaptive
enzymes in bacteria pose the problem as to how small molecules
induce the formation of a specific protein. Today, many workers
feel that enzyme adaptation is not under genetic control because
of the difficulties of explaining how it works by the current theory
of enzyme synthesis. This argument cannot be true, for it is well
established microbiologically, at least, that the ability to form an
adaptive enzyme is an inherited character, and unless there is
more than one way of inheriting a character, it must be under the
control of DNA. The thought arises then that perhaps something
is wrong with the theory of DNA function and protein synthesis.
It is possible for the various kinds of RNA found in a cell to be
breakdown products of one active form of RNA and the processes
observed in the test tube to be working in the opposite direction
to those in a living cell. Perhaps the aminoacids themselves recognize the DNA code and not the RNA, or perhaps both do, but
each perform a different function. The whole science of im-
munology tells us that one protein can code the formation of another protein and it seems to us that any large molecule is
potentially capable of coding another but incapable of coding the
sequences so essential to the proper functioning of a cell during
its lifetime before division. This is, undoubtedly, the function of
DNA, and proper genetic continuity rests not on the type of molecules made but on the inheritance of the correct sequences of
events. If this is true, how does the DNA control these sequences?

From our own work, it is possible to suggest how this might be achieved. First, however, it is necessary to review the major findings, and this is best done by their enumeration before a general discussion.

(1) In the aerosol, or desiccation at any RH level below 90 per cent, the free water is removed almost instantaneously and only 5 to 30 gms. of water/100 gms. of cell solids remains in the cell. This amount of water is shown to agree with the bound water content of a cell, or isolated DNA, RNA or protein, therefore, desiccation at different RH levels changes only the bound water content of cells.

(2) The death rate of air-borne cells is directly related to the amount of bound water removed, or more correctly, to the amount remaining in the cell. The log survival versus time of drying is a bilinear relationship at intermediate RH levels and an exponential one at 40 per cent RH or lower. Moreover, the rate of cell deaths during the second phase (one to five hours) is more affected by temperature change than is the death rate during the zero to one hour period. At temperatures below 20°C., the log survival versus time relationship at 30 per cent RH becomes a bilinear function.

(3) Thermodynamic analysis of the death rates obtained during the two periods at different temperatures indicates that death is due to a tightening of molecular structures and is associated with relatively small activation energies. The activation energies calculated agree well with those of other workers on the heat activation of dry microbes.

(4) No effects of oxygen was found in the presented studies, but, with the drums, minute amounts of oxygen may still be present. Those workers who have reported oxygen effects have used cells on filters and under vacuums of $10^{-2}$ to $10^{-6}$ mm/Hg where no water exists in the cell. Presumably the free radicals in the cell produced by such low vapour pressures can interact with oxygen.

(5) The rates of cell deaths decrease during the first ten minutes of the lag-phase of growth but increase sharply at about twenty minutes and then decrease again.

(6) Very few deaths occur at above 70 per cent RH but a sudden increase in the cell's sensitivity to desiccation occurs as the RH is lowered between 70 and 45 per cent. This sharp increase in sensitivity occurs between 70 and 55 per cent RH during the zero to one hour period, and between 55 and 45 per cent RH during the one to five hour period. Maximal death rates are found at 30 per cent RH or lower.

(7) Cells grown in minimal medium (MM) or aerosolized in the spent MM as a slurry are more stable than cells grown in a rich medium. The spent MM will, in part, stabilize cells grown in a rich medium.

(8) Air-dried cells may be stabilized by peptides and some aminoacids at 50 per cent RH and over. NaCl reduces their protectiveness and changes the RH at which maximal death rates occur from low RH levels to intermediate ones.

(9) Compounds possessing a six carbon ring nucleus and substituted --OH and --NH$_2$ groups will protect cells but may be toxic at RH levels above 60 per cent. All phenols or straight chain hydroxy compounds are toxic to air-dried cells, but the substitution of an --NH$_2$ group in the ortho position to the --OH group will render the compound protective at 30 per cent RH.

(10) The methylation or acetylation of protective --OH or --NH$_2$ groups destroys the ability of a compound to preserve the viability of the cell, so also will the simultaneous presence of NaCl, urea or any toxic compound. At the same time, however, the toxicity of the compound is reduced.

(11) The incorporation of one or two nitrogen atoms in the ring nucleus of dihydroxy aromatic compounds reduces their toxicity and produces a compound protective at low RH.

(12) Of the compounds examined, i-inositol is the best "all-round" protective agent in that it is not toxic at any RH and gives maximal protection at all the RH levels tested.

(13) With other cyclic compounds the relative positions of the substituted --OH and --NH$_2$ groups required to give maximal protection changes in accordance with the RH level at which the dried cells are held.

(14) On desiccation at 30 per cent RH, the number of re-

ducing groups in the cell is decreased and no peroxides are found. The former phenomenon is prevented by inositol.

(15) Changes in the reaction rates of various enzymes are found in desiccated cells but this is not prevented by inositol.

(16) Inositol stimulates the release of metabolites from dried cells and in particular, RNA. Desiccation at RH levels above 70 per cent without inositol does the same.

(17) Desiccated cells lose their ability to produce adaptive enzymes either temporarily or permanently. Inositol will prevent this loss of metabolic activity and will preserve the infectivity of virus sensitive to desiccation. The extent of loss of the former depends on the time of contact between the cell and the particular substrate before drying.

(18) The capacity of *E. coli* to produce the odd series of bacteriophages is partially destroyed by desiccation. The extent of damage depends on the particular virus and the RH at which the desiccation is carried out. Damage to the phage capacity occurs below 70 per cent RH only and is maximal at 40 per cent RH.

(19) All types of vegetative phages in infected cells of *E. coli* B are destroyed by desiccation below 70 per cent RH but the extent of damage depends on the post-infection time. Maximum stability of the vegetative phages occurs fifteen minutes after infection.

(20) Desiccation below 55 per cent RH produces various mutant cells and maximum numbers appear at 40 per cent RH. If drying is carried out in the presence of aminoacids, lactose, or as a slurry in MM, no aminoacid dependent or lactose negative mutants are found. Moreover, back mutants are not found if the cells are aerosolized from a suspension in the required metabolite.

(21) Inositol will prevent the inactivation of phage capacity and vegetative phage as well as production of mutant cells on drying.

(22) Air-borne cells may be killed by UV or visible light up to 5200A and the shape of the log survivor versus dose (or irradiation time) depends on the particular wavelength used, the RH at which the cells are held during irradiation, the light intensity at

humidities above 60 per cent, and the number of cells per aerosol droplet.

(23) There is a rapid increase in the sensitivity of cells towards light as the humidity is lowered from 70 to 55 per cent RH, but decreasing the RH below 55 per cent does not further increase the sensitivity. In addition, cells in aerosols are from ten to twenty times more sensitive to UV than cells suspended in liquids.

(24) The capacity of *E. coli B* to produce T odd phages is inactivated by light at RH levels below 70 per cent. The maximal rate of destruction is reached at 50 per cent RH and this remains constant at lower RH levels.

(25) The various vegetative phages in infected cells are inactivated by light but the extent of the inactivations depends on the RH at which the cells are held and the post-infection times. Vegetative phages exposed to UV within seven minutes after infection are almost as sensitive as the host cell, but fifteen minutes after infection they become much more resistant. The maximum rate of increase in the inactivation rates with respect to RH occurs as the RH falls from 70 to 50 per cent.

(26) Cells continuously irradiated with sub-lethal 3000 to 4000 A 'black light' show a reduced ability to manufacture adaptive enzymes and bacterial viruses provided that the irradiation is commenced within fifteen minutes after contact between the cell and the inducer molecule, or within fifteen minutes after infection with a virus.

(27) The black light slows down the uptake of basic aminoacids but has no effect on glutamic, aspartic, tryptophane, tryosine or phenylalanine. It also slows the uptake of thymine when the experiments are conducted in aminoacids. If the cells are irradiated in MM, thymine uptake is less affected.

(28) The uptake of aminoacids and uracil by starved cells shows two phases of incorporation. A rapid uptake during the first ten to fifteen minutes, then a lag phase of about ten minutes followed by a secondary uptake. Thymine uptake does not occur until phase one of aminoacid and uracil incorporation is complete but both phases of uracil and aminoacid uptakes will occur in a medium of aminoacids and glucose devoid of thymine using a thymine dependent strain of *E. coli*.

(29)  Air dried cells are more sensitive to x-rays at 70 to 80 per cent RH than at any other level of RH. So is the capacity to produce bacteriophages and the sensitivity of vegetative phage at the onset of infection. The x-ray sensitivity of these three things decreases rapidly between 70 and 50 per cent RH and also between 80 and 90 per cent RH. In addition, the sensitivity of vegetative phages increases with post-infection time and maximal resistance occurs fifteen minutes after infection.

(30)  Inositol will protect the cell, vegetative phages and phage capacity against x-ray damage at 80 per cent RH and below, but is less effective at 90 per cent RH. Thiourea and 2-aminoresorcinol will also protect at 30 per cent RH, but both are toxic to the cells at 60 per cent RH and over. X-ray damage and the toxicity of chemicals are not additive. Compounds such as DMS and sodium arsenite, while they protect cells against desiccation and UV light at low RH levels, will not prevent x-ray damage.

(31)  Inositol will prevent the inactivation by UV of vegetative phages, the cell's ability to produce adaptive enzymes and bacterial viruses as well as cell mutation and loss of viability. The degree of protection afforded these cell functions depends on the intensity of light used. High degrees of protection are found only when the intensities of light used allow an RH effect to be seen. At higher intensities, the RH effect is lost and so is much of the inositol protection.

(32)  Desiccation will induce the lysis of lysogenic *E. coli K12* and the production of Lambda phage. Maximum lysis, expressed as a percentage of the recovery of cells at zero time in aerosols occurs at 30 per cent RH. X-rays and UV will also induce lysis, the former is most effective at 80 per cent RH and the latter at 60 per cent RH. As the RH is lowered, smaller doses of UV are required to give the same degree of lysis but with x-rays higher doses are needed.

(33)  Tissue cultures infected with a virus or carrying a latent virus release them on desiccation at 40 per cent RH.

(34)  Inositol will protect normal animal cells against loss of viability during storage in liquids at 37°C., 25°C., 4°C. and liquid nitrogen temperatures, but seems ineffective in preserving

the viability of some tumor cells at liquid nitrogen temperatures and normal cells at $-20°C$.

(35) Animal cells protected with inositol release large amounts of RNA and some viruses.

(36) Normal animal cells dried at 40 to 70 per cent RH induce tumors in experimental animals and the maximal yield of tumors is obtained when animals are infected with normal cells dried at 40 per cent RH.

From this summary, it is plain that there are three consistant findings; first the rapid change occurring in the desiccation, UV or x-ray sensitivity of a cell or virus or cell function associated with the production of new proteins between 70 and 40 per cent RH; second, the increase in resistance of vegetative phages or ability to manufacture an adaptive enzyme towards all three physical agents fifteen minutes after infection or pre-incubation with a substrate before treatment; third, the ability of the same compounds to protect against desiccation, UV, and in some cases, x-ray damage. That we deliberately arranged our experimental conditions to show maximal effects of RH may be criticized, particularly as far as our non-ionizing radiation work was concerned, but this was done to demonstrate the similarities between the action of desiccation, toxic chemicals and radiations.

Like most other techniques, the aerosol is not as simple as it may first appear, but if handled properly it does overcome many of the difficulties of controlled drying at given cell water content levels experienced when filters or vials are used. Perhaps the most important technical detail is the type of spraying devise used. This must generate droplets of not more than $10\mu$ in diameter, or if larger droplets are utilized, smaller numbers of cells should be used. It seems absolutely essential to have a monodispersed aerosol in order to obtain reproducible results for, as has been shown, the number of cells per drop will affect the behaviour of the air-borne cells towards drying, chemicals, and radiations. If cells are dried on filters, then monolayers must be used otherwise different results will be obtained. Some authors have gone to great pains to study the effect of cell concentration on the rate of cell deaths due to drying alone using organisms extremely sensitive to drying. Most have found that high concentration of cells produced few deaths at 20 per cent RH and have concluded high concentrations to be the best to use. Naturally, little effect of RH or water content was observed because most of the cells were not dried or equilibrated with the environmental water vapour. The cell concentration used should have been the one at which the maximum death rate occurred without the radiations. If technicalities such as these are realized then few problems as far as reproducibility arise and the necessary confirmation of results from one worker to another become more readily achieved.

The thermodynamic analysis of cell death rates indicates that a tightening of molecular structures occurs when the cell is desiccated. The loss of reactive reducing groups and the absence of peroxides plus the loss of antigenic sites on the cell surface add up to an interaction between the oxidizing and reducing groups of cell structures. This is obviously made possible by the rearrangement or removal of structural water because inositol will prevent its occurrence. The question is whether these inter-actions are intermolecular or intramolecular ones? The latter hypothesis is favoured because we were unable to demonstrate any effect of drying on enzyme activity that was altered by inositol. Since inositol is able to prevent the death of a cell, any metabolic function altered by desiccation or irradiation under our experimental conditions and not affected by the presence of inositol (i.e., does not revert to that of the controls) must be discounted as a cause of death, or conversely, as a vital function of life. If we discount enzymes then we are left with lipids, RNA and DNA. As for the lipids, we know very little at this time although it is thought that lipoprotein complexes dissociate on drying. This could very well lead to cell damage particularly since lipoprotein —RNA and perhaps DNA complexes do occur. We have recently embarked on a study of microbial lipids and the effects on them of desiccation and irradiation but so far no real evidence for lipid damage has been found. Although their role in a cell seems to be mainly a structural one, their firm association with basic "histone-like" small proteins in some cells is becoming very clear. One apparent phenomenon is that the hydrophobic groups of lipids orientate water molecules between other molecules and it would seem that repulsive forces as well as attractive ones help in keeping water molecules in their correct position in and between macromolecules. Moreover, while extracted lipid is very rapidly oxidized outside the cell by UV light, lipids extracted from heavily irradiated cells show no evidence of oxidation, so perhaps their oxidation products are reduced by inter-actions with the reducing groups of other molecules. On the other hand, energy dissipation in the cell may be such that lipids remain unaffected. In any case, considerably more work is required before any sound hypothesis can be made on the role of microbial lipids as far as cell structure and function is concerned. If we discount lipids, for the time being at least, then we are left with the RNA and DNA.

Taking the RNA first, we know that desiccation will prevent or slow the formation of new enzymes as will x-ray and UV light, lethal or non-lethal. It is clear, also, that overactivity of the RNA may occur as a result of treating the cells with one or other of the three physical agents and inositol will prevent this as well as the inactivation of RNA viruses but brings about the release of RNA from a desiccated bacterial or incubating animal cell. Therefore, it is reasonably easy to postulate that the retention of damaged and over-active RNA leads to cell death but the question is why? Other workers, as mentioned in the text, have claimed over-active RNA to be lethal and their explanation is that an incorrect RNA-DNA ratio prevents DNA replication. As far as our work is concerned, we venture to suggest that the overactive RNA is due to the breakdown of normally inactive RNA with the production of unnatural aminoacid-RNA-complexes. This could result in the formation of inactive proteins through the production of the wrong kind of RNA and hence, lead to cell death.

We have examined the activity of ribonuclease both in dried and non-dried cells as well as UV irradiated ones, and have found the activity of the enzyme to be stimulated by drying and irradiation at 80 per cent RH in water or at 30 per cent RH in inositol. To examine this the treated or untreated cells were immediately sonically disrupted and the activity of ribonuclease in the sonic lysate measured over the next thirty minutes by removing samples at given intervals of time precipitating with 5 per cent TCA, and measuring the optical density at 260 m$\mu$ in the supernatant fluids. Six to ten replicates have so far been made, and in every case, the ribonuclease activity increased in inositol protected cells on drying or irradiation. Expressed in terms of $\mu$ g RNA/Mg dry wt of cells broken down in thirty minutes the values were: Dry 30 per cent RH, twenty-two; Dry inositol 30 per cent RH, forty-three; Dry 80 per cent RH, 38; Irradiated inositol forty-one; controls twenty. These values represent from 20 to 40 per cent of the total RNA in the cell and it is interesting to note that the amount of RNA released from animal cells suspended in inositol, or bacterial cells on drying in inositol was found earlier to be about 20 per cent higher than those in BSS or dried from water respectively, although this appeared to be high molecular weight material. It is evident, also, that the activity of the enzyme in the dry 30 per cent RH water group is the same as the controls, suggesting that the enzyme remains undamaged after the various treatments and the idea as to the retention of damaged RNA being responsible for some deaths to be incorrect. Also, this hypothesis does not explain the observed increase in UV or desiccation resistance of the vegetative phages or the cells ability to synthesize adaptive enzymes as the pre-incubation time before drying lengthens; the occurrence of mutants, or the prevention of the latter by the presence of the metabolites themselves. Nor does it answer the question as to why non-lethal 3000-4000 A light prevents adaptive enzyme synthesis, reduces phage production and prevents the incorporation of aminoacids if the cells are irradiated prior to fifteen minutes of incubation with the inducer molecule or infection with virus. Therefore, we looked to the DNA for our answers.

It seems very clear that the uptake of aminoacids during the first fifteen minutes is responsible for the stabilization of the vegetative phages and is necessary for host cell and perhaps viral DNA replication. At the same time, metabolites such as lactose preserve the ability of a cell to produce adaptive $\beta$-galactosidase and prevent the appearance of Lac$^-$ mutants. In addition, bacterial cells grown in minimal medium, presumably having all their genes in operation, are much more stable to desiccation and irradiation both as far as their viability and mutation rates are concerned. These facts, plus the observation that thymine uptakes are not suppressed to the same extent in MM during the first fifteen minutes by non-lethal black light suggests associations between the intermediate metabolites or the aminoacids themselves and DNA take place.

Bearing in mind the two phases of both protein and RNA synthesis, we tried the logic of the following explanation of our results. Correct genetic continuity was assumed to rely on the inheritance of intact sequences normally in order along the bacterial DNA or chromosome of higher organisms, and, therefore, we had to start with the Watson and Crick DNA double helix. At first, we thought that during the first fifteen minutes aminoacids and RNA bases affixed themselves in the two outer grooves of the structure, the bases attaching themselves in the deep groove and the amino acids or their precursors; sugars or their precursors; and perhaps lipids or their precursors molding into the shallow groove. In both cases, some water molecules were displaced while others were used to keep the correct configuration necessary. As a result of this the long distance H-bonds between the two halves of the DNA molecule would be severely affected and the halves would separate displaying the inner Watson and Crick code, thereby allowing DNA replication to occur. This idea aborted because we could see no reason why the formed RNA or protein should separate from the DNA, for if the build-up of RNA on one side and protein on the other opened the helix, then there was no physico-chemical reason for the inner code to attract new bases. In reconsidering the situation, we took into account that a cell on division not only receives DNA but also pre-coded RNA and, therefore, cells grown on MM are potentially capable of manufacturing amino acids without reference to the DNA.

All that was necessary, therefore, was to interpose a given metabolite between the DNA bases and the amino acids. If all the experimental facts are considered, it appears that the biologically active code of the DNA molecule is not only the base-pair H-bonds of the Watson and Crick model, but also the display of groups on the "outside" of the molecule. It is suggested, therefore, that the operational gene for enzyme production is a particular configuration on the outside of the DNA plus a given metabolite, and that in the absence of the metabolite the structural configuration is preserved by H-bonded water molecules which can be replaced by inositol or like compounds. If this particular DNA configuration is damaged by loss of water on desiccation or irradiation it will obviously affect the inner code when the two halves of the helix separate and deformed daughter DNA will result. The idea is schematically shown in Fig. 6-1.

A$_1$ and A$_2$ are meant to represent the deep and narrow grooves respectively on the outside of the intact double helix DNA molecule. In the various parts of the shallow groove, certain configurations exist which allow the attachment of specific small hydrated molecules or water. The exposed configuration of the DNA surface is altered by their attachment and protein formed on this will automatically be coded for the attached substrate. Also, the formation of the protein will result in the production of a specific RNA coded for the enzyme. The attachment of the substrates, proteins and RNA will seriously affect the strength of the base-pair H-bonds and the two halves of the helix will separate exposing the "inner" code. Because of the presence of protein (P$_1$) in the deep groove of the single strand, it will attract the necessary complimentary bases and form a new double helix with a narrow groove ready for action. Protein (P$_1$) is, therefore, considered to be a DNA polymerase whose internal energy is sufficient to activate an existing single strand of DNA and naturally it cannot function unless some DNA is present. The happenings on the other half of the original DNA molecule must be somewhat different. It is suggested that the action of the formed enzyme changes the original substrate and forms a new intermediatary compound resulting in the liberation of the coded RNA and the enzyme while the new metabolite is reorientated in the same site or is positioned in the next site along the DNA molecule (or more probably along a given chromosome). The latter process will allow a second daughter molecule to form plus new P$_1$ protein. The process will now repeat itself using the newly formed sub-

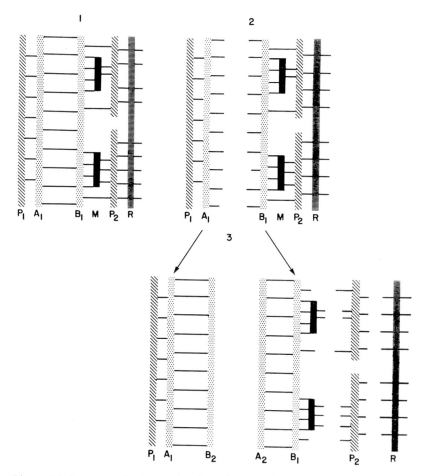

Figure 6-1 A suggested scheme showing why protein synthesis is necessary for DNA replication. A and B represent the two single strands of DNA. P represents proteins. R represents RNA. M represents metabolites (taken from Webb, *Nature 203,* 1964a).

strate. Since RNA coded for these various enzymes is being made and shed as the protein functions, it follows that on reaching the cytoplasm it will manufacture more enzyme molecules and protein synthesis as such will go on regardless of what is happening to the DNA. Moreover, if the RNA molecule is a double helix it will duplicate itself in the same fashion as proposed for DNA, the only difference between it and DNA will be that the duplication of the latter takes place in orderly sequence along the chromosomes so that the continuity of the linear arrays, so essential to the life process, is kept intact. There can be no doubt that the RNA carries out of the nucleus parts of these arrays intact, and it can only be assumed that the RNA viruses have reached a stage where their duplication is independent of DNA.

The above hypothesis fits the facts known about gene expression and protein synthesis. It follows that DNA duplication will rely on active protein synthesis, yet once started the latter process can occur without DNA. The necessity of linear array of genes governing the synthesis of a compound such as an amino acid, immediately becomes apparent as well as the mechanism by which DNA synthesis takes place in linear fashion on the chromosome. If such assumptions are made, the induction of enzymes becomes the normal method of protein synthesis rather than the abnormal one and our current ideas as to what is an adaptive enzyme are largely a matter of the kinetics of the reactions.

Apart from these physiological pointers the stability of a gene towards UV., x-rays and desiccation in terms of water content, growth medium and phase of growth are readily explained. If metabolites do act in combination with the gene, it follows that in the presence of the metabolite the gene and cell may be more stable and this is exactly what is found. Presumably the inactive genes are merely hydrated and hence, they are damaged more easily and it can only be assumed that their replication requires the correctly orientated water or attachment of a nonspecific molecule such as inositol. This could lead to the production of nonenzymic histones at biologically inactive sequences of gene sites which would be freed again when DNA replication occurred.

If the assembly of amino acids on the DNA is necessary for its replication, it follows that some cells, as is demonstrated below, may develop multiple blocks in amino acid synthesis on irradiation, and hence, only when an external supply of amino acids is supplied can the DNA replicate and the cells divide. If, as is usual, complimentary molecules exist in the cells, some of the progeny will receive DNA in which only the back mutation is apparent.

On the other hand, cells grown in minimal medium will possess pre-coded RNA capable of manufacturing the amino acids and these cells will not require an external supply.

As is generally accepted, a compound able to bind with the inner code may stimulate the incorporation of an incorrect base. However, irreversible binding of small molecules to the outer codes, or the loss of structural water could well lead to the distortion of the DNA molecule when it attempts to replicate. Also, compounds able to bind with the outer codes of RNA or DNA should be capable of inducing the synthesis of specific enzymes. In the studies reported, the fact that the cells in minimal medium slurries were so stable would suggest that the metabolites are not removed as a result of enzyme formation. However, it is well known that DNA synthesis goes on during about 80 per cent of the lifetime of a bacterial cell, so presumably most of the metabolites remain in position. The cell is small and there is little room to house all the formed enzymes and supplied metabolites, perhaps this is why it has such a short mean generation time.

Naturally, there are many alternatives to such a scheme. One is that the formed proteins do not separate from the DNA and hence, only one of the daughter DNA molecules with the open narrow groove will function. A second is that the proteins are not made in both grooves and the amino acid-RNA base complexes stretch across the DNA molecule or between complimentary DNA molecules with the aminoacid affixed to one groove and the RNA base in the other. The one big question is how a cell in minimal medium and previously grown in a rich medium produces enzymes necessary to manufacture amino acids before there are any amino acids. At this time, we can only fall back on the supposition of a small protein turnover and the carry-over of aminoacids in the cytoplasm at division. In addition, it is possible for the inorganic $NH_3$ plus the carbon skeletons, manufactured from glucose or first formed amino acids to arrange themselves in the same sites as a particular amino acid, but because the carbon skeletons are activated by different bases from those activating the amino acids themselves the formed RNA would be different and able to produce the enzymes needed for amino acid synthesis.

In the presence of aminoacids, however, their preferential adsorption to the DNA sites would lead to perhaps a 'histone-like' compound and an RNA capable of manufacturing in the cytoplasm a protein able to block the whole sequence of genes. The idea of the $NH_3+$ sugar skeleton stems from the fact that washed cells transferred from a rich medium + glucose to MM + lactose will not produce $\beta$-galactosidase unless amino acids are supplied.

In any event, the concept that the "outer" grooves of the DNA molecule have separate integrities and definite separate biological functions in the coding of RNA and proteins seems to fit not only the presented data, but most of the facts known concerning protein synthesis and gene expression. Considered from the standpoint of energetics and the shifts in ionic or H-bond strengths accompanying the attachment or liberation of metabolites from the DNA molecule, the above hypotheses seem not unreasonable. If the two phases of protein and RNA synthesis are real then the increased stability of vegetative phages and enzyme production towards desiccation and irradiation after short post-infection or inducer contact times would appear to be due to the uptake of amino acids and the production of specific proteins stable to the treatments. It is possible, also, for the attachment of aminoacids to the DNA, but before it commences to replicate, to induce a degree of stability, the latter would certainly seem true of the host cell DNA.

Our latest experiments have concerned themselves with the effect of 5 per cent inositol on amino acid, uracil and thymine uptakes by cells in MM. To date, uracil uptake and the incorporation of arginine, lysine, alanine and thymine all appear to be partially inhibited during the first fifteen minutes. In addition, the burst size of cells infected with T3 or T7 is increased by this high concentration of inositol if the compound is added to a full medium at the correct time. We take these findings as supporting evidence for our hypothesis that inositol, and other metabolites, combine with host or viral DNA and in so doing, assist in the separation of the two halves of the DNA molecule. Moreover, inositol either competes with amino acids for certain sites or produces an artificial hydrated structure to which the amino acids

cannot be attached. Possibly this is how, and why, the compound
protects cells against lethal physical agents. The findings can be
correlated with two phases of protein synthesis for while inositol
inhibits the uptake of uracil and some amino acids during the
early stages of cell growth, it does not appear to interfere with
the production of phage coat proteins or the secondary uptakes
of these two types of metabolite. In addition, if washed cells grown
in a full medium are infected with T7 phage and then transferred
to MM they appear unable to complete the synthesis of the virus,
so it would seem that the virus does attach itself to host DNA and
render it incapable of coding for amino acid synthesis.

The suggestion that the rate of cell deaths in aerosols versus
time of aerosolization at 50 per cent RH is a bilinear function is,
of course, incorrect. It is one of a continuously decreasing slope.
Nevertheless, the analysis of results in terms of two time intervals
enabled us to demonstrate that the death rate is determined by the
ease with which certain water molecules are removed. In a large
conjugate macromolecule, the structural water is held in position
by repulsive forces as well as attractive forces. Presumably, those
held by pressure or squeezing between hydrophobic groups are
the more easily removed, while the ease with which the bound
water H-bonded to macromolecular groups is lost will depend on
the strength of the particular H-bond. We assume then that at a
given RH the exchange rate between the environmental water
vapour and bound water will depend on these H-bond strengths
as well as the external vapour pressure defined in terms of RH and
temperature. Certain groups such as $-N$, or $-NH_2$, or $-OH$ will
be rapidly desiccated at high RH, whereas $=C=O$ or $=P=O$
groups will not. Therefore, the number of possible configurations
a partly desiccated macromolecule may assume will increase as
more water is removed. Some of these structures will be reversible

with water and allow the dehydrated cells to recover, others will be lethal, it follows, therefore, that the more bound water removed, in a given time, the higher becomes the number of lethal ones. That reorientation of water may be lethal is clearly demonstrated by the recent findings that cells in aerosols at 30 per cent RH are rapidly killed if the humidity is raised to 70 per cent. In fact, dried cells blown into an aerosol show maximal stability at 30 per cent RH and are rapidly killed at 70 per cent RH, just the reverse of cells aerosolized from suspension. If, however, dried cells are placed in water instead of water vapour, only a few deaths occur. Some of the deaths of the dried cells at high RH may be due to the heat produced when the vapour is adsorbed, but others are undoubtedly due to incorrect water addition products distorting the structure of essential macromolecules. In one very recent experiment, we have been able to show that quickly fluctuating the RH between 50 and 70 per cent is as lethal to cells as UV or x-rays (Fig. 6-2). Moreover, it seems clear that the action of toxic chemicals such as the various glycols relies on their ability to re-orientate bound water rather than replace it. The work of Wells (1955) demonstrates clearly that these compounds are only effective as air-disinfectants at 50 per cent RH and over, and the same is true of formaldyhyde. Also, the fact that compounds of the same type such as DMS will not prevent x-ray damage, suggests they do retain water in the cell.

The data obtained from the radiation experiments cited indicate that damage to a cell or virus due to x-rays follows an exponential function, whereas UV inactivations may not. In this kind of work, it is important to understand what an exponential relationship between dose and death means. Strictly it implies only that the number of cells dying in unit time is dependent on the number of survivors, and when one is dealing with populations in the millions it may not indicate that first order kinetics applies to the reaction responsible for death. It is possible to obtain exponential plots of log survivors versus time, chemical concentration or temperature as well as dose of radiation, but this does not mean the cells are killed by one chemical reaction following first order kinetics. What is actually measured is the sum

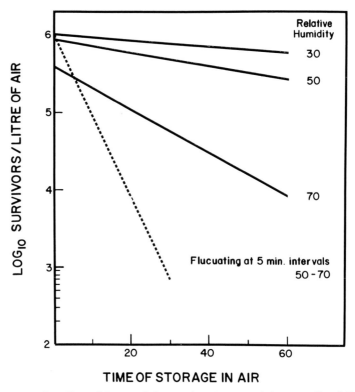

Figure 6-2 The effect of RH and fluctuating RH on air-borne cells of *E. coli* aerosolized as a dry powder.

total effect of many reactions, each of which may follow first, second, third or even partial order reaction kinetics. This, of course, is very evident from x-ray experiments where investigators know that indirect actions of oxygen and water occur as well as direct actions, each of which sets up a multitude of reactions and any one reaction is potentially capable of killing a cell, yet the exponential death rates are interpreted as a single reaction. The addition of all these reactions, not the individual chemical reactions, leads to an exponential log death versus dose relationship when the number of surviving cells is used as an experimental end point. This is not often realized when mathematics only are used to explain biological phenomena. Another possibility is the induction of types of pseudomonomolecular reactions where the biological integrity of a single macromolecule may be destroyed by different interactions with another single component in excess, and this would seem to be the case with water. It seems clear that the presence of over 30 gms. of $H_2O/100$ gms. of cell solids helps to prevent UV from killing or mutating a cell, and this may be the result of energy dissipation through the H-bonded water lattice. A certain amount of x-ray damage appears to be stopped in a like manner since at 90 per cent RH x-rays are less able to affect microorganisms than at 70 or 80 per cent RH. However, inositol seems to protect cells against UV by maintaining the structure of macromolecules by some mechanical means, for it is difficult to visualize energy migrations through this molecule unless the —OH groups become H-bonded intermolecularly forming a water-like lattice. Perhaps energy transfer damping; alternative energy transfer routes; and the maintainance of DNA or RNA structure by mechanical support all play a role in the protection of cells against drying, UV and x-rays by water or inositol. It is clear that protection by inositol is the direct result of its presence, instead of water, in some vital part of the secondary or tertiary structure of RNA or DNA.

As far as the target theory is concerned, its failure to describe the inactivation by UV of wet cells appears to be because the role of bound water, both in preventing and causing UV damage, or the influence of dose rate at low intensities has not been too well recognized. Even if these factors are taken into account there are other complications. The density of cells in aqueous suspension, on filters or agar blocks and the type of cell growth (e.g., clumping) can all influence the type of dose-response curves obtained.

As far as clumping is concerned, the sigmoid log survivor versus dose relationship is generally assumed to be the result of the need to kill every cell per clump before colony formation is prevented. However, the packing of *E. coli* cells in aerosol drops also results in sigmoidal curves even though the clumps break up during collection. It can only be assumed that cell-to-cell contact affords a degree of protection, either by lowering the surface to volume ratio and hence, altering the bound water content of the

cells at a given RH level or by physically lowering the effective
dose by the absorption of the radiations. If the latter is true, then
the sigmoidal nature of the log survivors versus dose curve is the
result of the relative concentration of sensitive to less sensitive
cells in a very large population. If the number of less sensitive
cells is greatly in excess of the more sensitive ones, and in view of
the experimental technique which makes it difficult to distinguish
between 2 and 4 x $10^6$ cells/litre of air, the initial slope of the
curve should be weighted towards the death rate of the less sensitive members of the population.

Any correlation between a "hit" number from UV or x-ray
experiments and the number of genes or chromosomes requires
much more knowledge than is presently available about the types
of small or large molecules associated with the DNA in a living
organism. As is shown in Chapter 4, small molecules such as
inositol or water can turn the same cell type from being perhaps
diploid at 30 per cent RH to a polyploid one at 30 per cent RH
or 80 per cent RH respectively which seems to be nonsense. By
the same token, action spectra on their own cannot be used to pin-
point the vital molecule damaged and are insufficient to argue
the reason for cell death. All that can be stated is that a compound
absorbing light of a certain wave-length may be damaged but it
must be realized that in a living cell there are many compounds
such as ATP, UTP etc., and free bases which have the same absorption spectrum as RNA or DNA. These could well be affected
by the radiations resulting in the formation of incorrect RNA or
DNA, certainly delayed mutation could be explained on this basis.
In addition, the absorption spectrum of a compound outside a
cell is often quite different from its spectrum inside a cell where
it is complexed with other molecules. Because of these factors, far
more knowledge of the molecular biology of cells than pure
physics is presently required in the interpretation of radio-biologi-
cal phenomena, and less arguments based on correlation to cause
with isolated cells systems, or the behaviour of individual metabolites. As stated earlier, it is repeatedly reported that the number
of cell deaths versus time or dose due to x-ray, UV, or perhaps
drying is an exponential function and a great deal of mathe-

matical importance is attached to such findings. However, this is a result of statistics, and exponential relationships would not be found if, for instance, 100 cells were used instead of $10^7$. Since there are at least three types of chemical reaction possible between cell macromolecules and the products induced by the x-radiations, and unless one assumes x-rays are selective, or the rate of reaction of each of the processes is the same, it is mathematically impossible to obtain an exponential death versus dose relationship, even if each reaction followed first order kinetics. Moreover, it is some-times claimed that the quantum yield for x-ray and death is unity. If it is, how does x-ray induce mutation? Simple considerations of this kind need to be undertaken before elaborate mathematical descriptions are applied. For the above reasons, it is quite evident that the exponential relationships found are really false ones as opposed to those of experiments with pure chemicals, especially when the relatively large experimental error, usually encountered in the determination of cell numbers, is considered. From the biological point of view, as far as the life or death of a microbe is concerned, the exponential relationships found may be de-scribed by the equation $N_t = N_o e^{-(K_1 + K_2 + K_3 \ etc) t}$ where $K_1$, $K_2$, $K_3$ etc., represent the individual reaction rates.

The idea of the thymine dimer as a reason for mutation or death is obviously a sound one but it must be backed by experi-ments designed to kill cells with radiation without dimer forma-tion and not repeated correlations between death due to one wave-length, large doses and mass destruction of cells. As far as our experiments have gone on this topic, the thymine dimer hypo-thesis does not seem to hold, for when cells are irradiated with the same wavelength, given the same dose over the same period of time, and the same number of cells die, dimers are only produced at low cell water content levels. However, it is possible that the amount of dimers necessary for death is too small to be detected. Supporters of the dimer hypothesis offer the demonstrated pro-duction of an enzyme capable of breaking the dimer as a reason for photo-reactivation or revival of some irradiated cells. Again, this is a correlation to cause argument, the test of such an idea is, can "dead" cells manufacture such an enzyme? There is every reason to suspect that they might for they can certainly produce adaptive enzymes, bacteriophages, and other viruses. From the standpoint of the physico-chemical stresses needed before dimerization could possibly take place in the DNA molecule, we feel that a cell is dead before these dimers occur, and the reason for the inactivation of a virus, a vegetative phage, or the cell itself, is the interaction between desiccated groups and semi-desiccated groups with the formation of foreign water addition products in those large conjugate macromolecules essential to the life of a cell.

If the ideas expressed above are true, then the biological integrity of a cell is completely dependent on the correct orientation and position of bound water molecules at the right times during its lifetime, and we should not consider biologically active proteins, RNA, DNA, or other macromolecules without their water, or the molecules with which they are associated inside the cell.

### Nature of Future Investigations

Perhaps, in summing up the results of our work so far, we have made some rather sweeping statements. However, our ideas at the moment, although a little different from currently accepted ones appear to fit not only our own data but also those of others, and seem to simplify rather than complicate many of the hypotheses concerning observed biological phenomena. Naturally, we intend to continue research in an effort to destroy our ideas and perhaps form new ones. Work is continuing on the action of black light, we would like to know why only some amino acids are affected, and what type of protein is made during the initial fifteen minutes of cell growth. At the same time, our research on animal cells and malignancy has assumed a larger proportion of our researches, as well as studies of the lysogenic and mutation phenomena in aerosols. As mentioned earlier, work has commenced on the action of x-rays, UV and desiccation on cell lipids, and the inter-relationships between bound water, oxygen, and x-ray damage. Moreover, we intend to continue our enquiries into dimerization, bound water and cell deaths.

The work over the past ten years has opened up so many lines of research that we cannot cover them all. As pointed out, properly handled with the correct spray, cell to drop ratio, and a lot of patience, the aerosol is an excellent scientific tool. Our hope is that the publication of this monograph will stimulate the interest of others and with their aid we will be able to add further knowledge to help us understand the apparent vital role of structural water in the life of a cell.

# REFERENCES

1. Arnoff, S.: Photosynthesis. *Botan. Rev.*, *23*:65-107, 1957.
2. Barer, R., and Joseph, S.: Refractometry of living cells. *Quart. J. Micr. Sci.*, *95*:399-423, 1954.
3. Bather, R., Webb, S. J., and Cunningham, T. A.: Evidence for the role of bound water and partial desiccation in carcinogenises. *Nature*. In print.
4. Bather, Sebastian, I., and Webb, S. J.: Inositol and the protection of cells. II. The release of nucleic acids from normal and malignant cells. *Canad. J. Biochem. Physiol.*, *42*:167-177, 1963.
5. Benzer, S.: Resistance to ultraviolent light as an index to the reproduction of bacteriophage. *J. Bacteriol.*, *63*:59-72, 1952.
6. Bergh, A. K., Webb., S. J., and McArthur, C. S.: *Histone-like Protein Bound to Lipid in Staphylococcus epidermidis.* To be published.
7. Bernal, J. D., and Fankuchen, I.: X-ray crystallographic studies of plant virus preparations. *J. Gen. Physiol.*, *25*:111-165, 1941.
8. Beukers, R., and Berencs, W.: Isolation and identification of the irradiation product of thymine. *Biochem. Biophys. Acta 41*: 550-551, 1960.
9. Blois, M. S.: Antioxidant determinations by the use of a stable free radical. *Nature 181*:1199-1200, 1958.
10. Briggs, D. R., and Hull, R.: Studies on protein denaturation electrophoretic study kinetics at neutrality of heat denaturation of $\beta$-lactoglobulin. *J. Am. Chem. Soc.*, *67*:2007-2014, 1945.
11. Buc, S. R., Ford, J. S., and Wise, E. D.: An improved synthesis of $\beta$-alanine. *J. Am. Chem. Soc.*, *67*:92-94, 1945.
12. Buchbinder, L.: Transmission of certain infections of respiratory origin. *J. A. M. A.*, *118*:718-730, 1942.

173

13. Bull, H. B.: Adsorption of water vapour by proteins. *J. Am. Chem. Soc.,* 66:1499-1507, 1944.

14. Cann, J. R.: The effect of binding ions and other small molecules on protein structure. *J. Phys. Chem.,* 63:210-217, 1959.

15. Cherry, W. B., and Watson, D. W.: The *Streptococcur lactis* host-virus system. *J. Bact.,* 58:601-620, 1949.

16. Cohen, S. S., and Barner, H. D.: Studies on unbalanced growth in *Escherichia coli. Proc. Nat. Acad. Sc.,* 40:885-893, 1954.

17. Cowie, D. R., and Robarts, R. B.: Electrolytes in biological systems. Edit. Shanes, A. M. Am. Physiol. Soc. 1-33.

18. Dawes, J. A.: *Quantitative Problems in Biochemistry.* London, Livingstone Ltd., pp. 40-41.

19. De Ome, K. B.: Effect of temperature and humidity and glycol vapour on viability of air-borne bacteria. *Am. J. Hyg., 40:* 239-250, 1944.

20. Dougherty, R. M.: The use of DMS for the preservation of tissue culture cells by freezing. *Nature 193:*550-552, 1962.

21. Dunklin, E. W., and Puck, T. T.: The lethal effect of relative humidity on air-borne bacteria. *J. Exp. Med., 87:*87-101, 1948.

22. Edsall, J. T.: The size, shape and hydration of protein molecules. *The Proteins.* Edited by Neurath, H. and Bailey, K., New York, Ac. Press Inc. *IB:*549-726, 1953.

23. Edsall, J. T., Edelhoch, H., Lontie, R., and Morrison, P. R.: Light scattering in solutions of serum albumin. *J. Am. Chem. Soc.,* 72:4641-4654, 1950.

24. Federoff, S.: Personal communication of unpublished data.

25. Ferry, R. M., Brown, W. F., and Damon, E. B.: Studies on the loss of viability of stored bacterial aerosols. *J. Hyg., 56:*125-150, 1958.

26. Ferry, R. M., and Maple, T. G.: Studies on the loss of viability of stored bacterial aerosols. *J. Infect. Dis., 95:*142-159, 1954.

27. Flaks, J. G., and Cohen, S. S.: Virus-induced acquisition of metabolic function. I. The formation of 5-hydroxy methyldeoxycytidilate. *J. Bio. Chem., 234:*1501-1506, 1959.

28. Flamm, W. G., and Birnstiel, M. L.: Studies on the metabolism of basic proteins. *The Nucleohistones.* Edited by Bonner, J. and TS'o, P. Holden-Day Inc., pp. 230-239.

29. Forbes, W. F., and Knight, A. R.: A study of hydrogen bonding and related phenomena by ultraviolet light absorption. *Canad. J. Chem., 37:*334-340, 1959.

30. Frank, J., and Livingstone, R.: Intra and inter-molecular migration of excitation energy. *Rev. Mod. Phys., 21*:505-509, 1949.
31. Friend, J. A., Harrop, B. S., and Shulman, J. H.: Influence of salt on the size and shape of protein-detergent complex. *Nature 168*:910-911, 1951.
32. Frossling, N.: The evaporation of falling drops. *Gerlands Beitrage Zur. Geophysil. 52*:170-216, 1938.
33. Fry, R. M., and Grieves, R. I. N.: The survival of bacteria during and after drying. *J. Hyg. Camb., 49*:220-228, 1951.
34. Gates, F. L.: A study of the bactericidal action of ultraviolet light. I. The reaction to monochromatic radiations. *J. Gen. Physiol., 14*:231-260, 1929.
35. Glasstone, S.: *Text Book of Physical Chemistry.* D. Van Nostrant Co., Ltd., 1950.
36. Goldberg, L. J., Watkins, H. M. S., Boerke, E. E., and Chatigny, M. A.: The use of a rotating drum for the study of aerosols over extended periods of time. *Am. J. Hyg., 68*:85-93, 1958.
37. Gordon, J., and Turner, G. C.: The protective effect of some carbohydrates against the inactivation of complement by heat. *J. Hyg., 54*:388-392, 1956.
38. Hale, A. J.: *The Interference Microscope in Biological Research.* London, Livingstone Ltd., 1958, pp. 74-81.
39. Harper, G. J., Hood, A. M., and Morton, J. D.: Air-borne micro-organisms: A technique for studying their survival. *J. Hyg. Camb., 56*:364-370, 1958.
40. Harper, G. J., and Morton, J. D.: *Bacillus subtilis* spores labelled with radiophosphorous. *J. Gen. Microbiol., 7*:98-106, 1952.
41. Harris, J. I.: The effect of urea on the enzymic activities of trypsin and chymotrypsin. *Biochem. J., 62*:28P, 1956.
42. Haurowitz, F., DeMoia, F., and Takman, S.: The reaction of native and denatured ovalbumin with congo red. *J. Am. Chem. Soc., 74*:2265-2271, 1952.
43. Henderson, D. W.: An apparatus for the study of air-borne infection. *J. Hyg. Camb., 50*:53-59, 1952.
44. Hotz, G. and Zimmer, G.: Experiments in radiation chemistry of T-1 phage. *Internat. J. of Rad. Biol., 7*:75-86, 1963.
45. Johnson, P., and Naismith, W. E. F.: The action of urea and guanidine hydrochloride upon arachin. *Trans. Fararay Soc., 52*:280-290, 1956.
46. Kaplan, R. W.: Genetics of micro-organisms. *Am. Rev. Micro biol., 6*:55-61, 1952.

47. Kaplan, R. W., and Kaplan, C.: Influence of water Content on UV-induced S-mutation and killing in *Serratia*. *Exp. Cell Res.*, *11*:378-392, 1956.

48. Klotz, I. M.: Protein interactions. *The Proteins*. Edited by Neurath, H. and Bailey, K., New York, Ac. Press Inc., *1*:743-744, 1953.

49. Klotz, I. M.: Protein hydration and behaviour. *Science 128*:815-822, 1958.

50. Koller, L. R.: Bactericidal effects of ultraviolet radiation produced by low pressure mercury vapour lamps. *J. Appl. Phys.*, *10*:621-630, 1939.

51. Koller, L. R.: *Ultraviolet Radiation*. New York. John Wiley & Sons, 1952.

52. Kornberg, A.: Biological synthesis of deoxyribonucleic acid. *Science 131*:1503-1505, 1960.

53. Kruyt, H. R.: *Colloid Science*. Elsevier Pub. Co. Amsterdam-London *1*:35-36, 1952.

54. Kunitz, M.: The kinetics and thermodynamics of reversible denaturation of crystalline soybean trypsin inhibitor. *J. Gen. Physiol.*, *32*:241-263, 1948.

55. Lauffer, M. A., and Carnelly, H. L.: Thermal destruction of influenza, a virus haemaglutinin. I. The kinetic process. *Arch. Biochem. 8*:265-274, 1945.

56. Lea, D. E., Haines, R. B., and Coulson, C. A.: The mechanism of bactericidal action of radioactive reactions. Proc. Roy. Soc., London B *123*:1-23, 1936.

57. Lester, W., Robertson, O. H., Puck, T. T., Wise, H., and Smith, M.: The rate of bactericidal action of triethylene glycol vapour on microorganisms dispersed into the air in small droplets. *Am. J. Hyg.*, *50*:175-181, 1949.

58. Levy, M., and Benaglia, A. E.: The influence of temperature and pH upon the rate of denaturation of ricin. *J. Biol Chem.*, *186*:829-847, 1950.

59. Loosli, C. G., Lemon, H. M., Robertson, O. H., and Appel, E.: Experimental air-borne influenza infection. *Proc. Soc. Exp. Biol. and Med.*, *53*:205-210, 1943.

60. Lovelock, J. E., and Bishop, M. W. H.: Prevention of freezing damage to living cells by DMS. *Nature 183*:1394-1395, 1959.

61. Low, B. W.: The structure and configuration of aminoacids, Peptides and Proteins. *The Proteins*. Edited by Neurath, H., and Bailey, K., New York, Ac. Press Inc. *IA*:356-361, 1953.

62. Mager, J., Kuczynski, M., Schatzberg, G., and Avi-dor, Y.: Turbidity changes in bacterial suspensions in relation to osmotic pressure. *J. Gen. Microbiol., 14:*69-74, 1956.
63. Maltman, J. R., Orr, J. H., and Hilton, N. A.: The effect of desiccation on *Staphylococcus pyogenes* with special reference to implications concerning virulence. *Am. J. Hyg., 72:*335-342, 1960.
64. McMeekin, T. L., and Warner, R. C.: The hydration of β lactoglobulin crystals. *J. Am. Chem. Soc., 64:*2393-2398, 1942.
65. McPhee, J. R.: Interpretation of properties of protein in concentrated salt solutions. *J. Phys. Chem., 62:*1455-1457, 1959.
66. Mitchell, P.: Transport of phosphate across the surface of *Micrococcus pyogenes. J. Gen. Microbiol., 9:*278-284, 1953.
67. Morton, J. D.: Personal communication, 1958.
68. Morowitz, H. J.: The action of ultraviolet light and ionizing radiations on spores of *Bacillus subtilis.* 1. The ultraviolet lethal action, mutation action and absorption spectra. *Arch. Biochem. Biophys., 47:*325-337, 1953.
69. Naismith, W.E.F., and Williams, R. K.: The effect of inorganic electrolytes on the denaturation of arachin with urea and guanidinium salts. *J. Polymer. Sci., 35:*465-473, 1959.
70. Neurath, H., Cooper, G. R., and Erickson, J. O.: The denaturation of proteins and its apparent reversal. *J. Phys. Chem., 46:*203-211, 1942.
71. Neurath, H., Greenstein, J. P., Putnam, F. W., and Erickson, J. O.: The chemistry of protein denaturation. *Chem. Revs., 34:*157-265, 1944.
72. Pankhurst, K. G. A., and Smith, R. C. M.: Some physical and chemical properties of gelatine-dodecyl sulphate complexes. *Trans. Faraday Soc., 43:*511-517, 1947.
73. Poirer, R. H., Kahler, E. J., and Bennington, F.: The chemistry of hydrazyl free radicals. *J. Org. Chem., 17:*1437-1445, 1952.
74. Pollard, E. C.: *The Physics of Viruses.* New York, Ac. Press Inc., pp. 103-121.
75. Pollard, E. C., and Dimond, A. E.: *The Physics of Viruses.* New York, Ac. Press Inc., pp. 113-114.
76. Pollard, E. C., and Reaume, M.: Thermal inactivation of Bacterial viruses. *Arch. Biochem. Biophys., 32:*278-287, 1951.
77. Putnam, F. W.: Protein denaturation. *The Proteins.* Edited by Neurath, H. and Bailey, K., New York, Ac. Press Inc. *IB:*807-892, 1953.

78. Richards, B. M.: X-ray diffraction and electron microscopic studies of nucleohistones. *The Nucleohistones.* Edited by Bonner, J. and TS'o, . Holden-Day Inc., 1964, pp. 108-116.

79. Robertson, O. H.: Air-borne infection. *Science 97:*495-502, 1943.

80. Robertson, O. H., Puck, T. T., Lemon, H. M., and Loosli, G. G.: The lethal effect of triethylene glycol vapour on air-borne bacteria and influenza virus. *Science 97:*142-144, 1943.

81. Rosebury, T.: Experimental air-borne infection. Baltimore, The Williams and Wilkins Co.

82. Ross, K. F. A., and Billing, E.: The water content of living bacterial spores and vegetative cells by refractive index measurements. *J. Gen. Microbiol., 16:*418-425, 1957.

83. Sahyun, M.: *Outlines of the Amino Acids and Proteins.* New York, Reinhold Pub. Co., 1948, pp. 125-130.

84. Schechmeister, I. L., and Goldberg, L. J.: Studies on the epidemiology of respiratory infections. *J. Infect. Dis., 87:*116-127, 1950.

85. Schwartz, N. M., and Strauss, B. S.: Effect of tryptophan analogues on the reversion of tryptophan-requiring strain of *E. coli. Nature 182:*888, 1958.

86. Scott, W. J.: Water relations of food spoilage organisms. *Advance Food Research 7:*83-84, 1957.

87. Scott, W. J.: A mechanism causing death during storage of dried micro-organisms. Symposium on Freezing and Drying. London, Institute of Biology, 1958.

88. Setlow, R. B.: Action spectroscopy. *Advances in Biol. and Med. Phys. 5:*37-71, 1957.

89. Setlow, R. B.: *Molecular Biophysics.* Addison-Westly Co., Ltd. 1962, pp. 298-299.

90. Sheehan, J. C., and Bolhofer, W. A.: A new isolation of hydroxylysine. *J. Am. Chem. Soc., 72:*2466-2468, 1950.

91. Shore, V. G., and Pardee, A. B.: Energy transfer in conjugate proteins and nucleic acids. *Arch. Biochem. Biophys., 62:*355-368, 1956.

92. Stent, G. S.: *The Molecular Biology of Bacterial Viruses.* W. H. Freedman & Co., 292-390, 1963.

93. Umana, R., Updike, S., Randall, J., and Dounce, A. L.: Histone metabolism. *The Nucleohistones.* Edited by Bonner, J. and TS'o, P., Holden-Day Inc. 1964, pp. 200-226.

94. Wacker, A.: Molecular mechanisms of radiation effects. *Progress in Nucleic Acid Research.,* New York, Ac. Press Inc. Vol. 1, pp. 369-399, .1963.

95. Wagner, R. P., and Mitchell, H. K.: *Genetics and Metabolism.* New York, John Wiley & Sons, 1955.

96. Waugh, D. F.: Protein-protein interactions. *Advances in Protein Chem., 9:*325-437, 1954.

97. Webb, R. B.: Physical components of radiation damage in cells. *Phys. Proc. Rad. Biol.,* edited by Augenstein, L., Mason, R., and Rosenberg, B. New York, Academic Press, 1964, pp. 267-282.

97a. Webb, S. J.: The counting of small numbers of bacteria in collecting fluids. II. The development of a radioactive tracer. Suffield Technical Paper No. 91, 1957.

98. Webb, S. J.: Factors affecting the viability of air-borne bacteria. I. Bacteria aerosolized from distilled water. *Canad. J .Microbiol., 5:*649-669, 1959.

99. Webb, S. J.: Chloramphenicol and the survival of air-borne bacteria. *Nature 183:*1072, 1959a.

100. Webb, S. J.: Factors affecting the viability of air-borne bacteria. III. The role of bonded water and protein structure in the death of air-borne cells. *Canad. J. Microbiol., 6:*89-105, 1960.

101. Webb, S. J.: Factors affecting the viability of air-borne cells II. The effect of chemical additives on the behaviour of air-borne cells. *Canad. J. Microbiol., 6:*71, 1960a.

102. Webb, S. J.: Factors affecting the viability of air-borne cells. V. The effects of desiccation on some metabolic systems of *E. coli. Canad. J. Microbiol., 7:*621-632, 1961.

103. Webb, S. J.: Factors affecting the viability of air-borne bacteria. IV. The inactivation and reactivation of air-borne *Serratia marcescens* by ultraviolet and visible light. *Canad. J. Microbiol., 7:*607-619, 1961a.

104. Webb, S. J.: The relationship between the structure of chemical additives and their action on air-borne cells. *Canad. J. Biochem. Physiol., 41:*868, 1963.

105. Webb, S. J.: Factors affecting the viability of air-borne bacteria. VI. The action of inositol on lactose oxidation by desiccated *E. coli. Canad. J. Biochem. Physiol., 41:*455-460, 1963a.

106. Webb, S. J.: The effect of relative humidity and light on air-dried organisms. *J. Appl. Bacteriol., 26:*307-313, 1963b.

107. Webb, S. J.: The effect of sublethal doses of artificial sunlight on adaptive enzyme synthesis by *E. coli. Canad. J. Biochem. Physiol., 41:*859-866, 1963c.

108. Webb, S. J.: Bound water, metabolites and genetic continuity. *Nature 203*:374-384, 1964.
109. Webb, S. J., Bather, R., and Hodges, R. W.: The effect of relative humidity and inositol on air-borne viruses. *Canad. J. Micro- biol., 9*:87-92, 1963.
110. Webb, S. J., Cook, C. A. M., and Bather, R.: Inositol and the pro- tection of cells. I. The release of nucleic acids and viruses from bacterial and mammalian cells. *Canad. J. Biochem., 42*:157- 166, 1964.
111. Webb, S. J., Cormack, D. V., and Morrison, H. G.: Relative humidity, inositol and the effect of radiations on air-dried microorganisms. *Nature 201*:1103-1105, 1964.
112. Webb, S. J., and Dumasia, M. D.: Bound water, inositol and the effect of x-rays on *Escherichia Coli. Canad. J. Microbiol. 10*: 877-885, 1964.
113. Webb, S. J., and Dumasia, M. D.: The effect of bound water and 2537A light on the production of Lambda Phage by air-dried *E. coli K12. Proc. West. Div. Can. M.R.C.,* 1965.
114. Webb, S. J., Dumasia, M. D., and J. Singh Bhorjee: Bound water, inositol and the biosynthesis of temperate and virulent bac- teriophages by air-dried *E. coli B. Canad. J. Microbiol.* In print.
115. Webb, S. J. and Singh Bhorjee, J.: The effect of 3000-4000A light and inositol on the synthesis of $\beta$-galactosidase and T7 coli- phage by *Escherichia coli* B. Can. J. Biochem. In print.
116. Wells, W. F.: *Air-borne Contagion and Air Hygiene.* Cambridge, Harvard University Press.
117. Wells, W. F., and Riley, E. C.: An investigation of the contamina- tion of air of textile mills with special reference to the in- fluence of artificial humidification. *J. Ind. Hyg. and Toxicol., 19*:513-561, 1937.
118. Wells, W. F., and Wells, N. W.: Air-borne infection. *J. A. M. A. 107*:1698-1703, 1936.
119. Wells, W. F., and Zapposodi, P.: The effect of humidity on $\alpha$ streptococci atomized in air. *Science 96*:277-278, 1948.
120. Williamson, A. E., and Gotaas, H. B.: Aerosol sterilization of air-borne bacteria. *Ind. Med. 11: Ind. Hyg.* Sec. *3*:40-45, 1942.
121. Witkin, E. M.: Time, temperature and protein synthesis: a study of ultraviolet-induced mutation in bacteria. *Cold Spr. Harbor Symp. On Quant. Biol. 21*:123-140, 1956.

122. Zelle, M.: The effects of radiation on bacteria. *Radiation Biology.* Edited by Hollaender, A., Vol. II, pp. 383-430, 1955.
123. Zelle, M., and Hollaender, A.: Monochromatic ultraviolet action spectra and quantum yields for the inactivation of T1 and T2 *E. coli* bacteriophages. *J. Bact., 68*:210-215, 1954.

# INDEX

## A
Activation energy
  death of bacteria, 16, 17, 18, 149
  inactivation of viruses, 18, 149
  protein denaturation, 19
Adenosine Triphosphate, 55
Adeno virus, 141-142
Adsorption isotherm, 22-23
Aerosol drum, 3-5
Alanine, 54, 108-110
Albumin, 13, 29
Alpha-methyl glucoside, 33
Aminoacids
  cell protection, 29, 30, 150
  decarboxylation, 54-56
  incorporation rates, 62-67, 107-110, 152, 157-158
  oxidation, 54-56
Amino phenols, 34-35, 50-52
2-Aminoresorcinol, 34-36, 45-52, 121-124
Amino uracils, 36, 50-52
Amnion cells, 134-135, 139-145
Antibodies, 83
Antigens, 83
Arachin, 52
Arginine, 29, 54, 108-110

## B
*Bacillus subtilis*, 7, 30-37, 99
Bacteriophages
  Synthesis by semi-dried cells, see Capacity
  Temperate, see lysogenic bacteria

Vegetative, see Vegetative Bacteriophages
Beta-galactosidase
  Synthesis by semi-dried cells, 56-67
  Synthesis by irradiated cells, 103-107, 131-133
Bound water
  Content of semi-dried cells, 11, 38-43
  and carcinogenesis, 134-145, 154
  and the destruction of bacteriophage producing capacity, 67-77
  and the destruction of vegetative bacteriophages, 67-77
  influence on radiation damage, 90-133
  and mutation, 77-83, 100-101, 124-133
  of proteins, 13, 38-43, 149
  and the rate of cell deaths, 11-24, 149
  and the structure of deoxyribonucleic acid, 85

## C
Capacity of cells to produce phages
  effect of drying on, 67-77, 151
  effect of radiations on, 102-107, 152
Carcinogenesis, 134-145, 154
Casein digest, 27-28
Chick embryo cells, 134-145
Chloramphenicol
  protection of cells, 44-45
  resistance to and cell stability, 44-45
Collagen, 13

## D
Death rate constants, 9

effects on the synthesis of bacteriophages, 67-77
effects on the synthesis of deoxyribonucleic acids, 56-67
effects on the synthesis of β-galactosidase, 56-67
effects on the synthesis of ribonucleic
acids, 56-67
and the preservation of animal cells,
135-138
protection of cells, 34, 35, 38, 44-52,
150-153
and radiation protection, 96-133, 153
and the release of viruses from animal
cells, 141-142
Interference microscopy, 38-43
Isoleucine, 29

**K**
Kinetics, 8, 10
death in aerosols, 164-167

**L**
Lactose, 54-56, 58-61, 80, 103
Leucine, 29
Leukemia, virus release from Erhlich
ascites cells, 140-145
Light scatter and water content of cells,
38-43
Lipids, 86, 155
Lysine, 29, 108-110
Lysogenic bacteria
effect of bound water content on induction of lysis by desiccation, 69-
77, 153
effect of bound water content on induction of lysis by irradiation, 114-
115, 119-120, 153
effect of inositol on induction of lysis,
69-77, 153

**M**
Mammary carcinoma, 142-145
Mannose, 33
Meta-aminophenol, 34, 35, 51
Methionine, 29, 108-110
*Micrococcus candidus,* 7
Mutation
by desiccation, 77-83, 151

influence of growth media on, 78-80
influence of inositol on, 79-82, 100-
101, 151
influence of metabolites on, 79-82
by irradiation, 100-101

**N**
N-acetyl glucosamine, 33

**O**
Orithine, 29
Ortho aminophenol, 34, 35, 51
Oxidation
of aminoacids, 54-56
of glucose, 54-56
of lactose, 54-58
Oxygen and cell death, 47, 82, 123, 149,
166

**P**
*Pasteurella tularensis,* 6
Peptides and cell protection, 30, 50-52,
150
Permeability, 55, 58, 60-63
action of inositol on, 55, 58, 60-63
changes in, 135-136
Peroxides
formation due to drying, 82
Phenols, 33
Phenylalanine, 29, 108-110
Phosphorus32 tracer cells, 7
Photodynamic dyes, 94-97
Pigeon Pox virus, 19
Proline, 29, 108-110
Proteins
and cell protection, 30
and the replication of DNA, 86-88
and synthesis by desiccated cells, 56-67

**R**
Reducing groups
action of inositol on, 82-83
effect of drying on, 82
Refractive index
measurement of water content of cells,
38-43
Rehydration, 23
Resorcinol, 36
Ribonucleic acids

## X

X-rays,
effect of dimethylsulphoxide on damage by, 118-133
effect of inositol on damage by, 118-133, 153

effect of sodium arsenite on damage by, 118-133
effect of thiourea on damage by, 118-133
influence of bound water on damage by, 115-118, 153